BIOCHEMICAL DETECTIVE STORIES

A Problem-Based Approach to Clinical Cases

BIOCHEMICAL DETECTIVE STORIES

A Problem-Based Approach to Clinical Cases

Mitchell L. Halperin
University of Toronto

Francis S. Rolleston
Medical Research Council
Ottawa

NEIL PATTERSON PUBLISHERS
Carolina Biological Supply Company
Burlington, North Carolina

Biochemical Detective Stories: A Problem-Based Approach to Clinical Cases

ISBN 0–89278–115–7

Printed in the United States of America: August, 1990

Typesetting is by LetroMac Desktop Publishing, Montreal, Canada.

NEIL PATTERSON PUBLISHERS
1308 Rainey Street
Post Office Drawer 2827
Burlington, North Carolina 27216-2827
U.S.A.
Telephone 800 227-1150
           919 226-6000
Facsimile 919 222-1926
Telex   574354
Cable   SQUID

ACKNOWLEDGEMENTS

We are very grateful to the following for their expert help in preparing this book: Bill Bridger, Sean Brosnan, Surinder Cheema–Dhadli, Aileen, Brenda, Frank and Ross Halperin, Lorne Jacobs, Jolly Mangat, Bob Murray and Rob Sladek

DEDICATION

With sincere appreciation to Brenda and Susan.

TABLE OF CONTENTS

SECTION 1

A FUNCTION-CONTROL ANALYSIS

SECTION II

METABOLIC PATHWAYS FROM THE PERSPECTIVE OF THEIR CONTROL

LIST OF CASES

FACTS CONCERNING KEY INTERMEDIATES

ATP: the energy currency

Glucose: the key intermediate in the circulation in the carbohydrate system

Pyruvate: the last intermediate inside cells in the carbohydrate syst em

Lactate: the equivalent of pyruvate in the circulation. It is an acid!

Glycogen: the storage form of carbohydrates

Amino acids: the intermediate in the circulation in the protein system

Triglyceride: the storage form of fat; it is abbreviated as TG

Fatty acids: the main intermediate in the circulation in the fat system

ß-hydroxybutyric acid: the potential fuel for the brtain derived from fat in the circulation. It is an acid!

Acetoacetic acid: the partner of ß-hydroxybutyric acid

Acetyl-CoA: the key intermediate in the fat system. It must be converted to ATP or fat.

PREFACE

Few textbooks dealing with the scientific foundations of the health professions have kept up with the evolution of teaching, which is becoming increasingly centered on problem-based learning, emphasizing concepts rather than facts. Most current textbooks of biochemistry seem to be aimed at honors biochemistry students. They are excellent compendia of biochemical facts and provide a good reference base for future detailed study of the subject. However, the needs of the student preparing for the health professions are different. Health professionals must relate a broad range of scientific disciplines to their patients'problems; they do not have time to learn a lot of ancillary detail that they may never use in their careers. They need guidance in how to select what is most important for them to learn, and they need instructional materials directly related to their requirements.

In working with students of the health professions over the past 20 years, we have learned that the physiological roles of the pathways of intermediary metabolism, and their controls, can be made clear without requiring students to learn, or even discuss, the enzymes or intermediates. A more detailed understanding requires, at most, some knowledge of the regulatory steps and their controls.

For example, the roles of glycolysis in energy metabolism are varied. It is the sole source of ATP in red cells and anaerobic muscle and the major source of substrates for the generation of ATP in the brain; its controls are, in effect, product inhibition by ATP. In brain in ketosis, glycolysis produces some of the substrate for the generation of ATP, sharing the honors with ketoacids; the controls are correspondingly more complex. In liver, glycolysis is a route for deposition of excess glucose as fat, and it also shares much of its pathway with the opposing gluconeogenesis; hence different controls operate. These physiological roles can be discussed with reference only to glucose, glycogen, lactate, pyruvate, and ATP, with the concepts of control by feedback inhibition and substrate supply, and discussion of controls by insulin. Thus, only simple facts and concepts are necessary to understand how the fuels, pathways, and controls are integrated into the functions of the major organs and the body; with these tools, the student can understand clinical cases involving these pathways.

This book applies this conceptual approach to clinical medicine. We focus specifically on the areas affected by the metabolism of the energy fuels - carbohydrates, fats and proteins. We seek to incorporate broad concepts of biochemistry and acid-base metabolism into an understanding of the physiology and nutrition of the whole body.

We build our discussion on clinical cases, chosen to allow introduction of the relevant concepts and facts. The reader is rewarded early in the book with an ability to deduce solutions to the cases presented; with the further cases, the reader can achieve deeper understanding in a cumulative manner.

In addition to presenting classical information in a new and selective manner, we have also tried to introduce new hypotheses that need to be verified. Examples include a possible approach to nutritional management of a patient with acute liver failure, which now results in close to 100% mortality, and introduction of a logic-tree approach to differential diagnosis of the pathophysiology of hypoglycemia or of metabolic acidosis rather than simply applying a standard battery of tests. We also integrate acid-base problems into disorders of energy metabolism, addressing such questions as how one might use an acid-base approach to spare lean body mass during prolonged starvation or how one might achieve the optimal therapeutic leverage in a patient with lactic acidosis.

The first half of the book is intended to be complete in itself. It uses some three dozen clinical cases to indicate the importance of the concepts being raised. This first part refers only occasionally to the classical metabolic pathways; the biochemicals mentioned are limited to the circulating fuels, the energy stores, pyruvate, acetyl-CoA, ATP, and NADH. These intermediates are the essential links among the five systems of energy metabolism; i.e., the carbohydrate, fat, and protein systems, the ATP generating system, and pyruvate dehydrogenase, the only single-enzyme pathway identified, are uniquely important due to its central role in conservation or consumption of glucose-potential carbon.

Chapter 1 includes 12 cases to present the fundamental concepts required to understand the use of energy fuels and their relation to the diet and to body stores. Chapter 2 broadens the conceptual base to include acid-base physiology, including the bicarbonate buffer system and the role of the kidney in excreting hydrogen ions and nitrogenous wastes. Chapters 3 through 6 then consider a wide range of clinical or normal situations in terms of the concepts raised and introduce quantitation of the amounts of the various fuels and wastes. The cases considered in these chapters include exercise physiology, diabetes, hypoglycemia and lactic- and keto-acidosis.

The second half of the book presents our view of the important aspects of the biochemistry of energy metabolism. It covers the pathways involved, with emphasis on their physiological functions and the relevant controls. Cases are also included to illustrate particular points of the pathways.

We have tried to arrange the format of the book to make it inexpensive and easy to use and to allow us to present not only the material we regard as essential but also additional material that embellishes and perhaps clarifies the central messages. The book is presented more in point form than standard text form; in this way, and by using boxed statements and other format strategies, we hope that the concepts are more easily comprehensible. We also present each page as a pair of facing pages; the main message is on the right page, with figures, embellishments, discussions of cases and diagrams on the left-hand page. In addition, we have scattered testing questions liberally throughout the text to help the student further determine the most important items to retain. To achieve the format we want and to minimize costs, we have worked with computer-based systems and provided the publisher with camera-ready copy.

We hope that readers at all stages of their careers in the health professions will find this book to be of value as they seek understanding of the problems presented by their patients. We have found that the approach in this book is of great value in teaching first-year biology or biochemistry students because it provides instant demonstrations of the relevance of biochemistry to their everyday lives. We are prepared to revise this book yearly to incorporate suggestions from readers. In this way, we hope to make it useful for students in all areas related to health sciences.

M.L. Halperin
University of Toronto

Francis Rolleston
Medical Research Council
Ottawa

FACTS CONCERNING KEY INTERMEDIATES

ATP
Adenosine triphosphate, the energy currency

Glucose
The key intermediate in the circulation in the carbohydrate system

Pyruvic acid
The last intermediate inside cells in the carbohydrate system

Lactic acid
The equivalent of pyruvic acid in the circulation. When it acculumates it can kill due to the load of acid!

Glycogen
The storage form of carbohydrates

Amino acids
The intermediate in the circulation in the protein system

Triglyceride
The storage form of fat; it is abbreviated as TG

Fatty acids
The main intermediate in the circulation in the fat system

ß-hydroxybutyric acid
The potential fuel for the brain derived from fat in the circulation. It is called a ketoacid.

Acetoacetic acid
The partner of ß-hydroxybutyric acid

Acetyl-CoA
The key intermediate in the fat system. It must be converted to ATP or fat.

CHAPTER 1

FUELS, TISSUES, PATHWAY AND CONTROLS

PART 1: ENERGY, FUELS AND STORES

Carbohydrates, fats and proteins are dietary fuels and stores of energy in the body. Fats are most efficient on a kcal per weight basis as energy stores.

Case 1–1   **Weight gain on a hypocaloric diet.**

Case 1–2   **Excess weight gain when regular exercise is interrupted.**

PART 2: ORGANS AND FUELS

The brain's need for glucose drives energy metabolism. Liver and adipose tissue maintain energy fuel supplies for consumer tissues, brain and muscle.

Case 1–3   **Confusion in a marathon runner.**

Case 1–4   **Death of a trauma victim.**

Case 1–5   **The liver quit!**

PART 3: INSULIN AND COORDINATION OF ORGAN METABOLISM.

Insulin coordinates energy metabolism, directing fuels to stores during meals and orchestrating the controlled release of stored energy between meals. Absence of insulin leads to uncontrolled release of these energy stores.

Case 1–6   **Normal dietary cycle**

Case 1–7   **Early diabetic.**

Case 1–8   **Suicide attempt with insulin.**

Case 1–9   **Dumping syndrome.**

PART 4: METABOLIC PATHWAYS AND CONTROLS

Fuels are handled through metabolic pathways and processes. If you know their function, you can deduce the controls.

Case 1–10   **Cancer cachexia.**

Case 1–11   **Weight loss in normal fasting.**

Case 1–12   **Hypoglycemia without hypoglycemia, the real world.**

SOME THINGS TO THINK ABOUT

- When you want to lose weight, should you lose fat or protein?
- What gives spectacular weight loss? Is it good for you? Will it stay off?
- What will cause a weight rebound after the diet?
- Why is the loss of weight so high in the first week of dieting?

BRIEF DISCUSSION OF CASE 1–1

This introduces the concept of "heavy and light" calories.

- Elizabeth was a little overweight when she went in for surgery.
- She had normal stores of protein and carbohydrate, but excess fat in her body.
- Because she did not eat during the 7 days after the operation, she was given a slow infusion of glucose, but less calories (100 kcal/day as glucose) than she was burning (1500 kcal/day). She would have lost her small stores of carbohydrate, and would have used some protein reserves and fat stores.
- Hence, when she started to eat protein, and resume activity, her body started to replace the lost protein and carbohydrate stores.
- Because she was eating fewer calories than she was burning (low calorie diet with little carbohydrate), she continued to burn fat.
- The protein and glycogen she was replacing weighed more than the fat she was using, because protein and carbohydrate are always stored with water (heavy calories), whereas fat does not contain water (light calories).

BRIEF DISCUSSION OF CASE 1–2

- Her usual vigorous morning exercise depletes her muscle of glycogen, therefore glycogen in muscle is low in the afternoon.
- Missing exercise in the morning allowed the glycogen in muscle to remain after her evening meal (0.4 kg of glycogen plus its associated water 0.6 kg).
- This "extra glycogen plus water" accounts for most of the difference in weight.
- The glycogen will disappear when she exercises again.

PART 1: ENERGY, FUELS AND STORES

- Chapter 1 is intended to be the foundation of this book. The remainder of the chapters expand on this framework.
- Chapter 1 introduces the 3 groups of energy fuels, the 5 major organs that use them, the 5 metabolic systems and the pathways they contain, and the major controls for the use of fuels by these organs.
- We use clinical cases or questions to illustrate the points we wish to make. Each case is outlined and only the essential facts are presented. At the end of the chapter, we invite you to reconsider all the cases in more detail, as a full understanding requires familiarity with all the material in this chapter.

CASE 1–1:
WEIGHT GAIN ON A LOW CALORIE DIET
(See facing page)

> Fats are much more efficient energy stores than carbohydrates or proteins.

Elizabeth underwent "routine" abdominal surgery, during which her bowel was "nicked"; hence she was not fed by mouth for 7 days. There was no infection; recovery was uneventful. She was delighted with the large weight loss (10 lb, 4.5 kg) and was determined to keep the weight off. To do so, she ate a low calorie diet containing protein with a small amount of carbohydrate. Intake of sodium chloride and fat was very low. To her chagrin, she gained 200 g (0.5 lb) per day. She asked her doctor why she had gained this weight. He said that she must have cheated on her diet. Being a nurse who was familiar with caloric intake, she knew this explanation had to be wrong, but "doctor is always right". Her response, depression with overeating, eventually "proved" the physician to be correct. But was he?

CASE 1–2:
WEIGHT GAIN WITHOUT EXERCISE
(See facing page)

Anne performs vigorous exercise each morning. She eats her major meal in the evening. She weighs herself each afternoon under the same conditions. Yesterday and today, she did not perform her regular exercise but ate and drank exactly as always. She noted a weight gain of 1.5 kg. Are Anne and the scale telling the truth?

FIGURE 1–1
ENERGY, ATP AND HEAT

The burning of fuels with oxygen conserves only about 50% of the available energy as ATP; the rest is lost directly as heat.

Some (very little) of the energy in ATP is conserved in body structures (which later become fuels). The rest of ATP energy is used for movement of all kinds, and is rapidly degraded to heat.

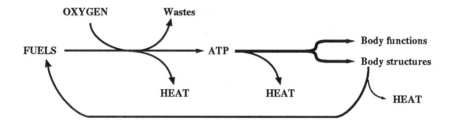

Weight of Stores

Comparison of the weight and caloric yield of stores

Muscle 1 pound → 400 kcal

Adipocyte 1 pound → 4000 kcal

Unit of Energy

The modern unit of energy is the joule, defined as the, amount of heat generated by a current of 1 ampere acting for 1 second against a resistance of 1 ohm. 1 Joule = 4.19 kcal.

The classical unit of energy in human nutrition is the calorie, defined as the quantity of heat required to raise the temperature of 1 g of water from $14.5^\circ C$ to $15.5^\circ C$. Units of energy in this book will be kilocalories (abbreviated as kcal).

ENERGY AND ATP
(Fig 1–1)

- Life requires energy. Energy is needed to build and maintain cell structures; to move, to reproduce, to think, to be alive.
- This energy must be provided continuously when and where needed, or life stops.
- Humans, and other animals, obtain energy from burning fuels with oxygen. The fuels come from the diet and are an enormous range of organic molecules. Most are incorporated for a time into body structures, but all are eventually burned for energy.
- Energy from burning fuels is conserved by making ATP, the energy currency of the cell. Processes requiring energy in the body get it by breaking down the ATP.

NEED FOR ENERGY STORES
(Fig 1–2)

- Fuels are provided to the body at meal times; meals may be irregular, and rarely in phase with major demands on energy.
- Every organ consumes energy all the time; in some, the rate can vary widely (energy use by muscle can vary 20–fold).
- Each meal is absorbed in 3 hours or so and on average contains more than enough energy fuels for the period until the next meal.
- A person keeping constant weight burns all the energy consumed each day.
- The blood contains only a few minutes' worth of energy fuels.
- Accordingly, energy stores are required. Dietary fuels in excess of immediate needs are packed away into stores, and released as needed between meals. Stores can contain months of fuel supplies.

FIGURE 1-2

FUELS AND ENERGY CONTENT

The figure illustrates the overall flows of nutrients in the four major metabolic compartments and the periods over which each can provide the energy requirements for the body.

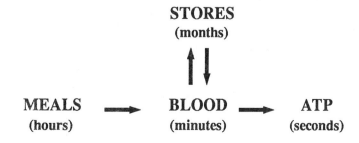

TABLE 1–1
BODY STORES, DAILY CONSUMPTION AND
TURNOVER OF ENERGY FUELS

	Content in grams dry weight			Duration of energy supply in stores
	Diet	Plasma	Body	
Fat	100	5	15000	150 days
Protein	100	240	6000	10 days
Carbohydrate	270	3	600	1 day

(The numbers are approximations.)

TABLE 1–2
ENERGY VALUE OF FUELS
(Summary)

Because carbohydrates and proteins are surrounded by water in the body (and in most foods) whereas fats are not, their wet and dry weight calorie contents differ. The marked differences in energy content per gram of fuel largely disappear when the energy released is related to the amount of oxygen consumed in burning these fuels.

	kcal/g dry weight		kcal/g wet	kcal released per g O_2
	accurate	usually cited		
Fat	9.3	9	9	3.3
Carbohydrate	4.1	4	1 – 1.5	3.5
Protein	4.1	4	1 – 1.5	3.1

Important questions concerning weight loss

1. Are salt and water being lost?

2. Are excessive calories being burned?

3. Was lean body mass lost as kcal in the urine?

4. Was an excessive quantity of lean body mass oxidized?

ENERGY FUELS, GENERAL
(Tables 1–1 and 1–2)

```
┌──────────────────────────────────────────┐
│            The Energy Problem              │
│                                            │
│   1.  Brain needs glucose as a fuel.       │
│   2.  Energy is stored primarily as fat.   │
│   3.  Fat cannot be converted to glucose.  │
└──────────────────────────────────────────┘
```

- Energy fuels are either carbohydrates, fats, or proteins.
- Fuels are eaten to provide energy; they also provide essential components of body structures.
- Carbohydrate and fat stores exist mainly as energy reserves.
- Proteins are structural or functional components of the body; they can be used as energy reserves, but only at the expense of their structure or function.

1. Fats

```
┌──────────────────────────────────────────┐
│  • Fat is the most efficient energy store │
│    because it is stored without water.     │
│  • The energy content of fat is 9 kcal/g.  │
│  • Fat cannot be used by brain except in   │
│    prolonged fasting.                      │
└──────────────────────────────────────────┘
```

Diet
- Examples of foods containing fat in the form of triglycerides are butter, vegetable oils or meat fats.

Storage forms
- Fat fuels (triglycerides) are hydrophobic. They do not mix with water and hence can be stored as globs of pure fat.
- Triglycerides are composed of 1 mol of glycerol and 3 mol of fatty acids. Oxidation of fatty acids provides the bulk of ATP.
  - Glycerol can be converted into glucose.
- Burning stored fats yields **9 kcal/g** weight.
- Fat serves mainly as an energy store; fat also helps in insulating and in cushioning delicate tissues.
- There is almost no limit to the amount of fat that the body can store.

ENERGY REQUIREMENTS OF HUMANS

The standard statement that a normal 70 kg person burns 2400 kcal/day is not much use, and sexist because it is based on figures for the average adult male.

Adult		Energy use in kcal/day
Normal females		1,700–2,000
Normal males		2,400–2,800
Bedridden patient eating normally		1,300–1,800
Newborn infant		350–450
Active teenager	Male	3,100–3,600
	Female	2,400–2,600

	Energy use for various activities (kcal/minute)*
Sitting at rest	0.7 – 2.0
Walking	2.0 – 6.0
Sprinting	15 plus
Long distance running	10 plus
Competition cycling	10 plus

* Rates vary with speed and body weight.

TABLE 1–3
BODY FUELS

Because of their water content, both proteins and carbohydrates are "heavy" calories, whereas fats are "light" calories.

Fuel stored	Dry weight of store (kg)	Water content of store (g/g dry)	Wet weight of store (kg)	Wet fuel energy content (kcal/g)	Total energy stored (kcal)
Triglyceride	15	0	15	9	135000
Glycogen	0.6	2–3	1.8	1–1.5	2400
Protein	6	2–3	18	1–1.5	24000

2. Carbohydrates

- Carbohydrates supply the largest part of dietary calories.
- Because they mix with water, carbohydrates yield 4 kcal/g dry weight after oxidation, but approximately 1–1.5 kcal/g wet weight.

Diet

- The foods containing carbohydrate are mainly polymers of glucose such as the starches (bread, flour, sweet corn, potatoes); they also occur in dimers (sucrose (table sugar), maltose (in beer), lactose (in milk)).

Storage Form

- Carbohydrates cannot exist in the body without water; hence they are "heavy calories".
- Dry carbohydrate yields 4 kcal/gram when burned. However, because of the need to pack away 2–3 gram of water for each gram of carbohydrate stored, each gram of stored carbohydrate–plus–water yields 1–1.5 kcal/g. Thus fats can store 6–9 times more calories per unit body weight than carbohydrates (Table 1–3).
- The major storage form of carbohydrate is the branched polymer of glucose, called **glycogen**. The body can store approximately 100 g of glycogen in liver (for release of glucose to blood) and approximately 500 g in muscle (for energy in muscle only).

3. Proteins

- Proteins are a "last resort" energy fuel.
- They mix with water; their energy content is 4 kcal/g dry weight but approximately 1–1.5 kcal/g wet weight.

Diet

- Proteins are a minor but essential part of the diet.

Storage Forms

- No proteins exist just as stores. All proteins have a specific function, such as enzymes, structural components (e.g. collagen) or hormones (e.g. insulin). Nevertheless, proteins form a large energy reserve owing to their mass.

BRIEF DISCUSSION OF CASES 1–3 TO 1–5

The Confused Marathon Runner
(See page 11 for more discussion)

In brief, Jon's muscles consumed the fuels that were needed by his brain. Therefore there was not a sufficient supply of fuels to permit his brain cells to synthesize enough ATP for their needs.

The Trauma Victim
(See page 11 for more discussion)

- For an unknown reason, some patients, like Joe, do not release sufficient fat–derived fuels to the circulation (like Elizabeth did in Case 1–1).
- Joe's rapid weight loss indicates use of heavy calories (protein in muscle) for almost all his energy needs, because insufficient fat was available.
- The brain continued to demand glucose, made in liver from amino acids derived from muscle.
- The rest of his body required his muscles to be burnt, since insufficient energy was available from fat.
- He died because he was too weak and immobile to clear his lungs of fluid that accumulated.

The Liver Quit!
(See page 12 and 13 for more discussion)

- Nutritional management must replace the handling of energy fuels by the liver.
- Two major functions the liver performs are:
  - It maintains a concentration of glucose in the blood that is sufficient to meet the needs of the brain.
  - It prevents the accumulation of materials that will threaten the body.
- The most important dangers are the accumulation of either H^+ (lactic acid) or ammonium (NH_4^+).
- Might it be possible to persuade the brain to oxidize lactic acid?
- Might it be possible to diminish the rate of production of ammonium in the body?

PART 2: ORGANS AND FUELS

The following cases allow consideration of the forms in which energy fuels circulate in the blood, and of the major organs which use these fuels.

> • **The brain's need for glucose drives energy metabolism.**

CASE 1–3:
THE CONFUSED MARATHON RUNNER

Jon entered the stadium for the final lap of his marathon race. He was well ahead of the pack. In the last minute or so, he seemed to become confused. In the stadium, he started running in the wrong direction around the track, and then collapsed. What went wrong?

CASE 1–4:
DEATH OF A TRAUMA VICTIM

Joe was badly injured in a motorcycle accident, suffering multiple fractures and severe internal injuries. He could not move or eat. Despite intravenous feeding, he lost weight rapidly, and died 15 days later. The death certificate said that he died of pneumonia (infection in his lungs). What happened?

CASE 1–5:
THE LIVER QUIT!

> • The liver maintains the concentration of glucose in the blood in the normal range.
> • Liver converts fatty acids to ketoacids when insulin is lacking, and at a rate proportional to the concentration of FFA in the blood
> • Independent of meals, liver converts lactic acid to glucose.
> • Liver detoxifies ammonium via the synthesis of urea.

Vic, a surgeon, pierced his finger with a needle while performing an operation on a patient with infectious hepatitis (viral inflammation of the liver, a disease which is readily transmitted by needles). Over the next week, Vic became severely ill with acute and massive destruction of most of his liver cells. When the case was discussed, it was decided that Vic could survive only if the nutrition team could do the jobs of the liver and maintain ATP balance in other organs for the next 7 days. What advice might be given?

FIGURE 1–3
OVERVIEW OF ORGANS, FUELS AND
THEIR FUNCTIONS

The fuels have a hierarchy of use. Fat is used first if available, then ketoacids and finally glucose if neither fat nor ketoacids are available.

CONSUMER ORGANS AND THEIR FUELS

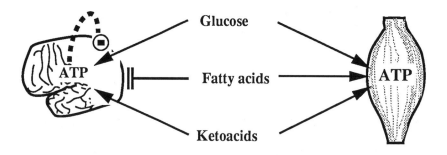

MAINTAINER ORGANS AND THEIR FUELS

Maintainer organs process surplus fuels, and make brain fuels when their supply is low.

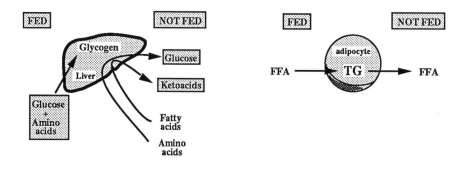

MAJOR ORGANS IN ENERGY METABOLISM (Fig 1–3)

The Paradox

- **There is little storage of glucose owing to its bulk, yet glucose is necessary as a fuel for the brain between meals because the brain cannot oxidize fatty acids.**

The dominant organs in energy metabolism are brain, muscle, liver, adipose tissue and kidney. These 5 organs are emphasized in this book. They can be divided into categories based on their function.

- Consumer organs – consume energy for their own purposes.
- Maintainer organs – ensure "consumer tissues" have the fuels they need.

CONSUMER ORGANS

Since these organs (brain, muscle) use fuels only to make ATP, the need to supply ATP regulates the use of these fuels. Control is exerted by negative feedback by the concentration of ATP, often mediated by related compounds.

Brain

- **Brain cannot burn fatty acids as they do not cross the blood–brain barrier.**

- Uses 20–25% of normal resting daily energy.
- Requires a supply of fuel and oxygen from the circulation to meet its constant need for ATP.
- Always requires glucose, usually 5g/hour.
- Can burn ketoacids for 80% of its energy if they are available in the blood.
- Has no store of energy.
- There is no direct role for hormones in its energy metabolism.

Muscle

- Energy use varies widely (20–fold) with degree of exercise.
- Muscle must not deprive the brain of its fuels.

- Uses 20–80% of total energy metabolism.
- Burns carbohydrate or fat fuels.
- Major reserve of body protein, because it is the largest organ.
- Contains significant carbohydrate reserves (glycogen) for its own use.
- Must spare brain fuels (glucose, ketoacids) during severe and prolonged exercise.

TABLE 1–4
ENERGY METABOLISM IN
IMPORTANT ORGANS
A quantitative perspective

The supply of blood and the consumption of oxygen in the major organs at rest and during exercise are provided.

ORGAN	Blood Flow l/min	O_2 Consumption mmol/min	Comments
Brain	1.0	2.7	– Constant uptake – 25% of resting energy use
Liver	1.0	2.0	– Relatively constant use – 15% of resting energy use
Kidney	0.7	2.0	– Energy demand depends on the filtered load of sodium
Muscle			– Large increase with exercise
– rest	1.3	3.3	
– exercise	10	150	
Adipose Tissue	0.2	0.1	– Very small rate of turnover of ATP
Other			
Rest	0.8	2.9	– Intestines, skin, heart
Exercise	5	10	– Mainly heart and skin
Total			
Rest	5	14	– Considerable reserve
Exercise	18	170	– Now near upper limit

MAINTAINER ORGANS

Maintainer organs (liver and adipose tissue) regulate the concentrations of fuels in the blood. They dispose of excess fuels from diet, and provide fuels between meals. They interconvert fuels so that the brain always has enough fuel to burn from the circulation. The main fuels for the brain are glucose and ketoacids so more will be made if their concentration in the circulation falls.

Adipose Tissue

- The body's "gas tank" Stores fat from blood triglyceride.
- Releases fat as free fatty acids.

Liver

- The body's "metabolic traffic cop". It regulates levels of fuels for the brain in the blood.
  - Regulates levels of glucose by storing and releasing glucose (as liver glycogen), and making glucose from precursors (amino acids) as needed.
  - Provides ketoacids when glucose is low.
  - Converts glucose to fats for storage when glucose is in excess.
  - Removes lactic acid produced by other organs.
  - Is the initial site of oxidation of unique fuels (eg. ethanol).
  - The detox center; detoxifies drugs, by–products, etc.

EXCRETORY ORGANS

- These organs use ATP to excrete wastes.

Kidney

- Excretes the non–volatile wastes, nitrogen (as urea and ammonium) and H^+.
- Metabolism is finely tuned to the need to excrete the excess acid formed during energy metabolism.
- Also, lungs exchange CO_2 for O_2 (see Chapter 2).

Overview of Energy Demands in Principal Organs

A summary of the demands for energy in the 5 principal organs is presented in Table 1–4.

TABLE 1–5
HIERARCHY OF OXIDATION OF FUELS

ORGAN	FUELS	COMMENT	QUANTITIES/DAY

• BRAIN	• Not FFA
	• Ketoacids
	• Glucose
		• FFA cannot enter brain
		• Ketoacids are elevated
		  only in prolonged fasting
			• 500 kcal
			• 120 g glucose used
			  unless ketoacids
			  present

• MUSCLE	• FFA
	• Ketoacids
	
	• Glucose
	
	• Branched–chain
	  amino acids
		• FFA burnt if supplied
		• Ketoacids not burnt if
		  FFA high
		• Glucose burnt if no
		  FFA or ketoacids
		  are available
		• Used during meals
			• Can vary 20–fold over
			  short periods.
			• Usually 800 kcal/day
			  in a sedentary person

• LIVER	• Amino acids
	
	• Ethanol
	
	• FFA
	
	• Glucose
		• Excess amino acids
		  are converted to
		  glucose
		• Ethanol is oxidized
		  to acetic acid
		• Use FFA if there is a
		  lack of glucose
		• Glucose is converted to
		  fat, rarely to CO_2
			• 400 kcal/day
			• Metabolic inter–
			  conversions produce
			  ATP; liver's need for
			  ATP might limit the
			  use of all fuels
			
			• Little oxidation of
			  glucose

• KIDNEY	• Lactate
	• FFA
	• Ketoacids
	• Glutamine
		• Lactate is main fuel
		  unless FFA or ketoacids
		  are high
		• Glutamine is the fuel
		  during acidosis
			• 400 kcal/day
			• Work related primarily
			  to ATP used to
			  reabsorb filtered
			  sodium.

ENERGY FUELS IN BLOOD

The energy fuels circulate in the blood in a number of chemical forms.

1. Carbohydrates circulate as:

- **Glucose** derived from diet or from liver.
  - Always required for synthesis of ATP in the brain. Ketoacids can replace some of the brain's need for glucose.
  - Is stored in, and released from, glycogen in liver.
  - Is stored in muscle glycogen, but can then only be used in muscle; it cannot be released as glucose from muscle.
  - Is used for the synthesis of ATP in all tissues.

- **Lactic acid** derived from muscle or red cells can be burned in kidney or converted to glucose in liver or kidney.
- **Glycerol** derived from stored triglyceride is converted to glucose in liver.

2. Fats circulate as:

- **Fatty acids** are released from adipose tissue triglyceride.
  - Can be converted to ketoacids in liver.
  - Can be burned to ATP in liver, muscle and kidneys.

- **Ketoacids** are water–soluble fat fuels.
  - Made in liver from circulating fatty acids without meals.
  - Can be burned for a source of ATP in brain or kidney and used sparingly in muscle.

- **Triglycerides** are in lipoprotein "envelopes".
  - From diet or made from glucose or amino acids in liver, carried to adipose tissue or muscle.
  - Stored primarily in adipose tissue, but also in muscle.

3. Proteins circulate as:

- **Amino acids**, the 20 building blocks of proteins.
  - Can be deposited in and released from protein.
  - Can be converted to glucose in liver (also the kidney in acidosis).

FIGURE 1–4
RED BLOOD CELLS USE GLUCOSE
TO BURN FAT, INDIRECTLY

We show this example to illustrate that one must look at the entire picture (process) to understand what is going on. The red cell needs ATP to do its work. It makes ATP and lactic acid from glucose. The lactic acid is converted to glucose in the liver. The ATP needed for the synthesis of glucose comes from the oxidation of fat.

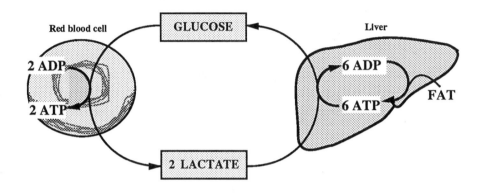

FIGURE 1–5
INTERCONVERSION OF FUELS

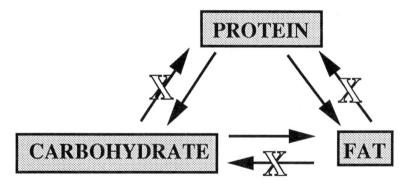

CHOICE OF ENERGY FUELS

1. **Many factors influence the body's choice of energy fuels.**

   - Needs of tissues
     - Brain and red cells always need glucose; red cells burn fat, indirectly (Fig 1–4).
     - Other tissues can burn most fuels.
   - Dietary supply
     - Carbohydrates are plentiful in normal diet but are limiting in fasting.
   - Efficiency as energy store
     - Fats are largest and most efficient energy store.
     - Carbohydrate stores are very limited.
     - Proteins reserves are large, but all proteins are functional. Hence their use as a supply of energy will impair body functions.
   - Interconversion of fuels (Fig 1–5)
     - Proteins cannot be made from either carbohydrates or fats, but can be made into both.
     - Fats can be made from both carbohydrates and proteins but cannot be converted back to either.
     - Carbohydrates can be made from proteins and can be used to make fats.

2. **These factors help define some basic concepts of energy metabolism**

   - The central dilemma of fasting
     - Brain always needs glucose.
     - The largest energy stores are fat.
     - Fat cannot be made into glucose (Fig 1–5).
   - Priorities for use of fuels
     - What for?
       - Satisfy immediate needs for ATP.
       - Replenish stores if fuels are available in diet.
       - Store excess as fat.
     - Which fuel?
       - Conserve glucose whenever possible.
       - Spare body protein whenever possible.
       - Burn fat for energy whenever possible, unless protein or carbohydrate are in dietary excess.

MARATHON RUNNER

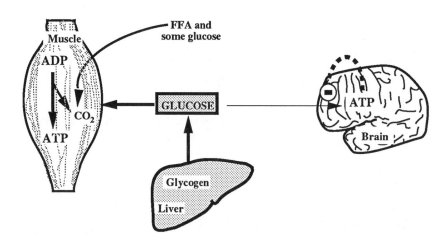

Excess use in muscle takes glucose from brain. Normally glycogen in liver will replace it, but at the end of the race, liver glycogen and muscle glycogen also are depleted.

TRAUMA VICTIM

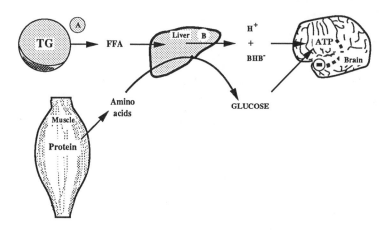

- The problems are either less FFA released from adipocytes (A) or less ketoacids formed in the liver (B).
- To avoid excessive breakdown of lean body mass, sufficient calories must be supplied to meet daily needs. To suppress protein catabolism, insulin should be administered.
- ß–HB = ß–hydroxybutyrate, the ketoacid that is most abundant.

CASES 1–3, 1–4 AND 1–5
IN A BIT MORE DETAIL

CASE 1–3:
MARATHON RUNNER GETS INTO TROUBLE

- The brain can use glucose or ketoacids.
- Ketoacids are not available as Jon is not starved. Hence only glucose can fuel his brain.
- Muscle can use fatty acids or glucose for energy. High use of fatty acids requires their efficient delivery to muscle, and also efficient delivery of oxygen. If either is lacking, glucose will be used.
- The marathon run has consumed body reserves of glucose.
- At the end of the race, Jon, striving for his personal best, is pushing his resources to the limit. A slight over demand on glucose can deplete blood and starve the brain of this energy source.
- Chapter 3 explores use of energy in muscle further.

CASE 1–4:
DEATH OF A TRAUMA VICTIM

- Again, brain can only use glucose because the response of normal fasting to release fat and make ketoacids has not operated in Joe.
- After 24 hrs, reserves of glycogen in liver are gone. Glucose can only come from gluconeogenesis in liver, using carbon from muscle protein.
- Hence most of the needs for ATP in Joe are coming from muscle protein, which break down rapidly. The brain consumes 1 kg of muscle to meet its daily need for ATP.

> 1 kg muscle = 200 g protein
> 200 g protein = 120 g glucose (not all amino acids nor all their carbons can be converted to glucose)
> 120 g glucose = brain's fuel need

- When close to half the body protein (muscle) is consumed, Joe will be too weak to cough up secretions. These will linger in his lungs, become infected and Joe will die with a diagnosis of bronchopneumonia on post–mortem examination. This death should have been prevented. How would you have prevented this tragedy?

VIC'S LIVER QUIT

WITH A LIVER

VIC'S PROBLEM

The problems are indicated in the boxes with shading

CASE 1–5:
VIC'S LIVER QUIT

THE PROBLEM

Mortality from massive failure of the liver with normal conservative management is close to 100%. There is no recommended therapy. Therefore we must be unconventional.

THE NEED

Keep Vic alive during the acute liver dysfunction in the hope that the liver will recover with time.

THE FACTORS

Vic is too sick to eat. Hence he must function with endogenous fuels and whatever you give him IV.

The liver's normal functions in energy metabolism are to:
- Produce glucose from glycogen or protein.
- Produce ketoacids from fatty acids during fasting.
- Remove lactic acid from the circulation.
- Detoxify NH_4^+ from the breakdown of amino acids by making urea.
- Liver also does other things we will not consider.

With the sick liver, none of the above occur. Results include:
- Hypoglycemia:
  - Low insulin; therefore
    - High release of fatty acids from adipose tissue.
    - High release of amino acids from protein.
  - The adrenaline response to hypoglycemia accentuates the above problems.
  - Breakdown of protein and triglyceride further stresses the liver.
- Accumulation of lactic acid.

Continued on page 13

CASE 1–5:
VIC'S LIVER QUIT
(continued)

TREATMENT WITH LOW GLUCOSE
AND INSULIN

There are 4 main actions of insulin, (the latter 2 effects are not shown)

• Prevention of release of FFA

• Accelerated net synthesis of protein

• Promotion of the conversion of glucose to glycogen

• Accelerated transport of glucose into muscle.

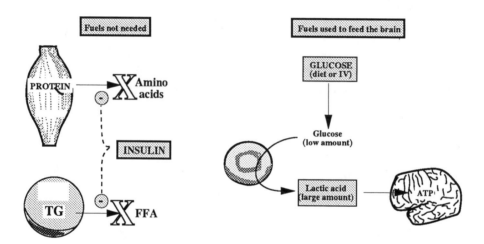

ADDITIONAL POINT

The release of ammonium might be reduced further by infusing the ketoacid analogues of essential amino acids and by infusing insulin with the hope of driving the synthesis of proteins from amino acids.

$$\text{Ketoacid analogues of amino acids} + NH_4^+ \rightarrow \text{amino acids} \xrightarrow{\text{(insulin)}} \text{protein}$$

VIC'S LIVER QUIT
(continued)

POSSIBLE TREATMENT for Vic

- The first problem is fuel for the brain.
  - There are no ketoacids and little or no glucose.
  - Hence the simple routine response is to give glucose, to keep its level at about 5 mmol/l.

> However, use of glucose involves production of lactic acid (from red cells, muscle, other tissues) and the sick liver cannot reconvert this lactic acid to glucose.

- Hence, lactic acid will accumulate in blood and can become lethal above 20 mmol/l; this may be a major factor in high mortality with conservative management.
- Brain can burn lactic acid if its concentration in blood is high enough (5–10 mmol/l) and glucose is low (1–2 mmol/l).

Hence, possible therapy is to provide glucose IV to keep blood lactate in the 5–10 mmol/l range; more glucose if lactate falls, less if it rises. Use the anion gap as a quick indicator of the concentration of lactate (see Chapter 6 for details).

- The second problem is NH_4^+. This will accumulate from breakdown of amino acids released from proteins due to low insulin levels.
  - Insulin should be given to limit breakdown of proteins. This will also limit breakdown of triglycerides and increase dependance on glucose and lactic acid (see Part 3 for more discussion).

Thus a possible treatment for Vic might be to give glucose at a rate determined by the concentration of lactic acid, and give insulin at levels to maintain low levels of amino acids in blood.

RAPID OVERVIEW OF CASES

CASE 1–6: (See page 17 for more discussion)
NORMAL DIETARY CYCLE
- Release of insulin, the hormone of the fed state, responds to increased concentrations of glucose and controls their distribution to various tissues.
- Most of the glucose is directed to stores, glycogen in liver and muscle (majority). Amino acids go to protein very quickly and fats to triglyceride more slowly.
- Ultimately, everything that is eaten must be oxidized in the steady state.

CASE 1–7: (See page 19 for more discussion)
EARLY DIABETIC
These are the classic signs of insulin–dependent diabetes mellitus. They arise because the ß–cells of the pancreas can no longer release the proper amount of insulin in response to a given concentration of glucose in the blood.
- The body reacts as if it were in uncontrolled starvation, irrespective of dietary intake or the concentrations of fuels in the circulation.
- Stores of fat and protein are rapidly broken down, causing high concentrations of fatty acids, ketoacids and glucose in the blood.
- Amino acids are made into glucose, and fatty acids into ketoacids.
- Glucose and ketoacids appear in urine, requiring excretion of water and salts.
- Mary lost weight quickly because of the catabolism of muscle protein, which is stored with water in cells (heavy calories).

CASE 1–8: (See page 20 for more discussion)
ATTEMPTED SUICIDE BY INSULIN OVERDOSE
- The excess of insulin causes glucose, amino acids and fat to be stored in tissues.
- The continuing concern is for fuel for the brain.
- Glucose should be administered by mouth if possible, or intravenously if necessary.

CASE 1–9: (See page 21 for more discussion)
DUMPING SYNDROME
- The stomach acts as a reservoir releasing nutrients to the intestine slowly.
  The surgery upset the reservoir function leading to 2 major problems.
  1. The small intestine received large amounts of very concentrated solutions of nutrients, causing water movement from the blood to the intestine via osmosis. This led to a fall in blood volume and symptoms of feeling faint and sweaty.
  2. The very rapid absorption of sugar led to hyperglycemia, causing excess release of insulin which led to hypoglycemia 2 hours or so later, a brain problem.

PART 3: INSULIN AND COORDINATION OF ORGAN METABOLISM

CASE 1–6:
NORMAL DIETARY CYCLE

> • Insulin coordinates energy metabolism; it directs energy storage and release.

Henry, a yuppie but not an athlete, strictly controls his weight through diet. He knows how hard it is to lose weight since he was rather podgy before he was forced to correlate his career goals with his personal appearance (see Case 1–11). He eats regular balanced meals, with no snacking.

How do the organs of his body work together to use the energy fuels provided in the diet?

CASE 1–7:
EARLY DIABETIC

> • Absence of insulin signals starvation, whatever the diet

Mary, 10 years old, started to lose weight fast, and pass large volumes of urine, while eating and drinking excessively. Why?

CASE 1–8:
ATTEMPTED SUICIDE WITH INSULIN

Algernon tried to commit suicide with an overdose of insulin. He injected so much insulin that its actions should persist for 24–48 hours. He is now alert, though he was confused a little while ago until glucose was administered. There are no other special features in this case. You are called by the physician in charge to help with the nutritional management:

CASE 1–9:
DUMPING SYNDROME

> • Stomach protects the body from excesses of the diet

Eric had gastric surgery for an ulcer. Once he got back on oral nutrition, he had unpleasant symptoms after meals, becoming dizzy, nauseous, light–headed and anxious, and then later even blacking out at times. What happened?

PRODUCT INHIBITION AND SUBSTRATE STIMULATION

A notation is needed to indicate the control effects on reactions. We use the following:

Reactions or pathways go from a **substrate (S)** to a **product (P).**

A controlling influence can act on any enzyme, and is indicated by a broken line with a + or − sign, indicating activation (speeding up) or inhibition (slowing down).

Thus

Note: These "control lines" indicate only the overall influence in general terms. It does not imply a direct mechanism.

Other effectors of a reaction: This notation can be used readily to indicate the effects of a third chemical on the reaction.

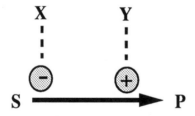

⊖ indicates that an increase of X will inhibit the conversion of S to P, either directly, or indirectly because X influences other chemicals (by activating or inhibiting other reactions).

⊕ indicates that an increase of Y will activate the conversion of S to P, either directly or indirectly.

CONTROLS

The rest of this book centers on controls over energy metabolism.

• **Metabolism** is the general word for the processes interconverting chemicals in life.

• **Controls** over metabolism are obviously necessary, e.g. to:
  – Control the rate of formation of ATP.
  – Allow net synthesis or breakdown of energy stores as needed.
  – Select the preferential fuel for synthesis of ATP.
  – Determine how much of a fuel in the diet will be stored directly, or converted to another storage form, or burned for ATP.

• **Homeostasis** describes the overall effects of control. Homeostasis implies:
  – Internal stability despite widely fluctuating rates of supply or demand.
  – Relatively constant levels of glucose or amino acids in blood despite large intermittent dietary loads.
  – Relatively constant intracellular level of ATP despite 20–fold rates of muscle activity.

Homeostatic controls can be expected to be self–limiting (see facing page).

Two overall types of control are:

1. Stimulation by a substance of its own use (**substrate stimulation or positive feed–forward**). Use increases when the level of this substrate rises and decreases when its concentration returns to normal.

2. Inhibition of a reaction by its own product (**product inhibition or negative feed–back signals**).

Signals

Controls over rates of metabolic processes are exerted through concentrations of chemicals in the body. Two major types of signal systems are readily identified:

– Pathway metabolites.
– Non–pathway metabolites
– Hormones via intracellular signals.

Acute vs Long–term Control

Acute control: This occurs before there is time to change the concentrations of enzymes. It is mediated a by a change in activity of existing enzyme molecules.

Long–term control: Time has permitted the synthesis or breakdown of enzyme molecules.

INSULIN AND GLUCOSE

The balance between storage and release of fuels is set by insulin and glucagon, which are determined mainly by levels of glucose in the blood.

Low glucose causes less release of insulin and more release of glucagon, causing:

- Higher release of fatty acids, thus less oxidation of glucose (Fig.1–6).
- Less storage and oxidation of glucose, thus less use of this compound (Fig 1–7).

FIGURE 1–6
MOST IMPORTANT ACTION OF INSULIN
ON THE OXIDATION OF GLUCOSE

By promoting the storage and preventing the release of FFA from adipocytes (A), insulin sets the stage for the oxidation of glucose in muscle (less ATP derived from fat fuels). Insulin aids the oxidation of glucose by permitting glucose to enter muscle cells (B).

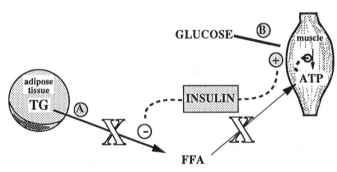

FIGURE 1–7
MOST IMPORTANT ACTIONS OF INSULIN
FOR THE PRODUCTION OF GLUCOSE

The first and key precursor of glucose in the circulation is glycogen in liver. Secondary sources of glucose are protein and glycerol derived from triglyceride. Should glycogen in muscle break down, lactate will be released and converted to glucose.

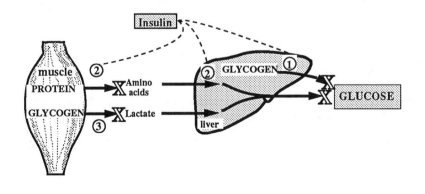

INSULIN CONTROLS OVER
ENERGY METABOLISM

> • Insulin is the fed state hormone. High insulin signals tissues to store fuels and not release them.

• Though glucose exerts the main control over insulin, probably the most important direct effect of increased insulin is to inhibit the release of fatty acids from adipose tissue.

• Insulin release from the endocrine pancreas (the ß cells of the islets of Langerhans) is stimulated by increased concentration of glucose. Insulin stimulates the use of glucose. Hence, glucose and insulin form a self–limiting control system.

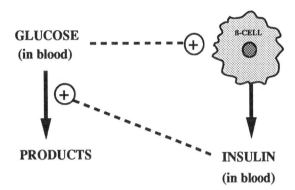

INSULIN AND ENERGY STORES

HIGH INSULIN

Stimulates Storage of Energy Fuels

• Glucose to glycogen (liver, muscle)

• Glucose to fat (liver, adipose tissue)

• Amino acids to protein (liver, muscle and other organs).

• Circulating triglycerides to storage fat (adipose tissue).

LOW INSULIN

Stimulates Release of Energy Fuels from Stores

• From glycogen in the liver to glucose in the blood.

• From adipose tissue triglycerides to free fatty acids in the blood. Liver converts some FFA to ketoacids.

• Muscle protein to amino acids in blood which are then converted to glucose in liver.

TABLE 1–6
FUELS AND WASTES IN A BALANCED DIET

FUELS

	MOL		WEIGHT	
			(g)	**(kcal)**
Carbohydrate	1.5	(as glucose)	270	1080
Protein	1.0	(as amino acid)	102	408
Fat	0.36	(as fatty acid)	104	936
Oxygen	21.6		690	–
Total fuels	–		1166	2424

WASTES

Carbon dioxide	18.7	821	–
Water	17.8	320	–
Urea	0.5	30	–
Ammonium	0.04	0.7	–

FOOTNOTE 1: Approx 100 moles (1.8 liters) of water are also taken in the diet as associated fluid or as drinking water.

Note: The weight of oxygen consumed exceeds that of carbohydrate, fat, and protein.

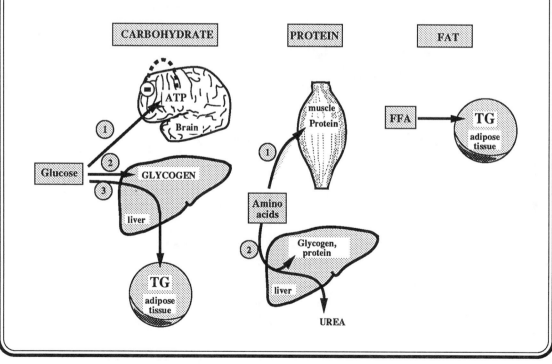

CASE 1–6:
NORMAL DIETARY CYCLE
(Case described on page 14)

> • A high level of insulin directs dietary fuels to stores; a low level leads to accelerated, but controlled release of these stores.

As he sits down to eat, Henry has been without food since he finished absorbing his last meal, several hours before. His glycogen stores in liver are therefore partly depleted.

Intake of food provides fuels for the next 8 hours; absorption takes approximately 2–3 hours. Thus Henry must store 5–6 hrs worth of fuel.

During Meals

> Priorities "During meals" are:
> • Provide fuels for brain (glucose) and other tissues;
> • Replenish stores of glucose (glycogen in liver and muscle) and of proteins burned since the last meal;
> • Store excess energy as fat.

The daily diet contains more than twice as much glucose as is needed for brain (Table 1–6). Thus, levels of glucose in the blood rise during the absorption of dietary fuels (e.g. from 70 to 150 mg % (4 to 8 mmol/l)). This stimulates release of insulin.

> Increased levels of insulin in blood signal:
> • Deposit glucose as glycogen in liver and muscle;
> • Deposit amino acids as proteins;
> • Deposit triglycerides into adipose tissue;
> • Convert excess energy fuels (glucose or amino acids) to triglycerides in liver and deposit them in adipose tissue;
> • Prevent release of fatty acids from triglyceride energy stores.

These signals of insulin limit the increase in glucose, amino acid and triglyceride in the blood caused by intake of food.

The decreased levels of fatty acids in blood reduce the rate of oxidation of fatty acids, thus favoring use of glucose (see Part 4 and Fig 1–6).

Continued on page 18

ENERGY FLOWS DURING MEALS

TABLE 1–7
A QUANTITATIVE DESCRIPTION OF
ENERGY METABOLISM IN THE BRAIN

The flow of blood to the brain is close to 1 liter/min or 1500 liters/day. The fuel menu for the brain is the same in the carbohydrate and protein phases of fasting; it changes markedly in the ketotic phase of fasting.

Fuel Used	Concentrations in Blood (mmol/l)		Consumption (production) (mmol/day)	A-V (mmol/l)	Source of ATP %
	Artery	Vein			
"During and Between Meals"					
– Glucose	5.0	4.35	650–700	– 0.65	100
– Lactate	1.0	1.4	(600)	+0.4	0
– Ketoacids	0.05	0.05	0	0	0
– Oxygen	8.0	5.3	4000	– 2.7	100
"Without meals": Ketotic Phase of Fasting					
– Glucose	3.5	3.2	500	– 0.3	20
– Lactate	0.7	0.9	(300)	+ 0.2	0
– Ketoacids	5.0	4.5	750	– 0.5	80
– Oxygen	8.0	5.3	4000	– 2.7	100

Footnote 1: Subtract half the output of lactate to deduce how much glucose was oxidized completely to CO_2 + ATP.

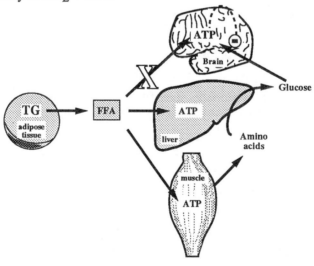

CASE 1–6:
(Continued)

ENERGY FUELS BETWEEN NORMAL MEALS

The priorities "Between meals" are:
- Provide energy fuels for brain (glucose) and other tissues.
- Conserve glucose as far as possible.
- Use fat stores for as much energy as possible.

After the diet is absorbed, the concentration of glucose in the blood returns to normal; therefore so does the concentration of insulin in the circulation.

Low insulin permits the controlled release of energy stores.

- The normal level of insulin during fasting allows a net release of fuels from stores, at rates controlled by the remaining levels of insulin (glucose) in the blood.
- The control of most importance to brain is the release of glucose from glycogen in liver, to match the use of glucose by the brain.
- The concentration of ketoacids remains low (they were kept low by the high insulin levels during the meal and take several days to rise without meals). Therefore, brain relies totally on glycogen in liver between meals (see Table 1–7).
- To conserve glucose for the brain, the rest of the body burns fat for as much of its energy as possible. The lowered levels of insulin allow release of adipose tissue triglyceride as fatty acids to blood; these can provide energy for most of the rest of the body.
- Oxidation of fat to yield ATP prevents organs from oxidizing carbohydrates. This is the basis for the hierarchy of fuels (fat is used first if it is available).

ENERGY FUELS BETWEEN MEALS

CASE 1–7:
EARLY DIABETES MELLITUS

CARBOHYDRATE LIMB

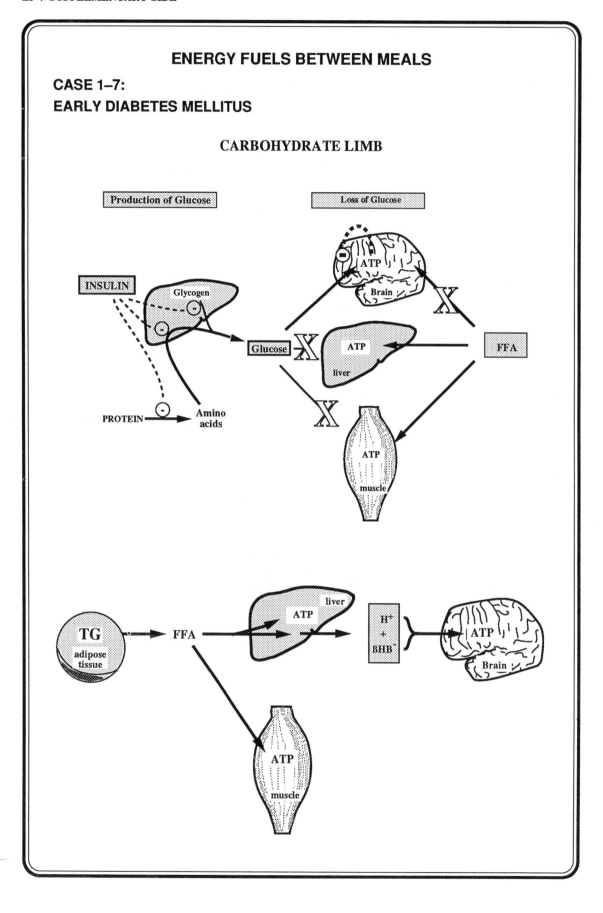

DISCUSSION OF CASE 1–7:
EARLY DIABETES MELLITUS
(Case described on page 14)

(see facing page)

- In a normal person, release of insulin is matched, minute–by–minute, to the concentrations of glucose in blood.
- Diabetes mellitus results when the pancreas does not release sufficient insulin in response to a high concentration of glucose in the blood. With destruction of the ß–cells of the pancreas, as in insulin–dependent diabetes mellitus, there is no insulin.
- By the time symptoms show in Mary, much of her endocrine pancreatic function is already gone.
- Without insulin, the normal balances of deposition in, and release from, stores swing to zero deposition and rapid release.
  - Rapid breakdown of adipose tissue triglycerides releases fatty acids and glycerol. Oxidation of FFA prevents the oxidation of glucose. The glycerol is converted to glucose in liver. Some of the fatty acids are converted to ketoacids in liver.
  - Rapid breakdown of glycogen in liver exhausts this store rapidly. Of continuing concern is the inability of liver to store circulating glucose while continuing to produce it. The net result is a very high concentration of glucose in the blood.
  - Rapid breakdown of proteins in the body (muscle is the major source) releases amino acids to blood. These are rapidly taken up, mainly by liver, and converted to glucose.
  - Breakdown of heavy (and light) calorie stores cause the rapid weight loss.
- The large increases in fatty acids and ketoacids in blood inhibit oxidation of glucose (see Part 4), thus further aggravating the hyperglycemia.
- Without insulin, oxidation of glucose by muscle is also limited (in rapid exercise, conversion of glucose to lactic acid may be rapid, but this does not remove carbohydrate carbon (Fig 1–4).
- The resulting hyperglycemia and hyperketonemia exceed the ability of the kidney to reabsorb them from the glomerular filtrate. Thus they are excreted, and require excretion of water and electrolytes – hence thirst and a low circulating volume.

The rapid weight loss results from:

1. Loss of protein (heavy calories) to provide the small amount of glucose needed by brain and the large amount excreted.
2. Loss of water associated with heavy calories and also to permit urinary excretion of glucose and ketoacid anions.
3. Loss of fat to provide all energy other than that for brain, plus to provide the excreted ketoacids (a minor consideration).

FAT LIMB

CASE 1–8:

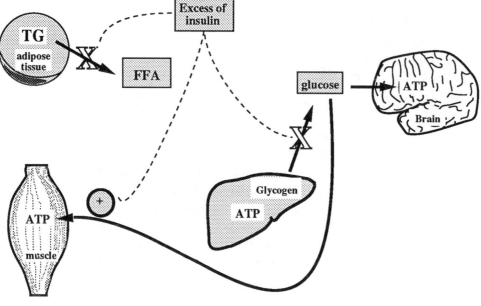

Notes:

Intravenous glucose is usually given as 50 g glucose per liter (at the osmolality of plasma). The provision of 25 g of glucose per hour to meet the total energy needs of the body will require the infusion of 12 liters of water. This will overtax the ability of the kidney to excrete water. Therefore:

1. Give more concentrated solutions of glucose or feed the patient by mouth.
2. Give ß-hydoxybutyrate (ß-HB) as this is an excellent fuel for the brain and it will not be made by the liver. This can be accomplished by giving, 1,3–butanediol, a precursor of ß-HB that does not use the regular pathway of ketogenesis in the liver (the precursor is an alcohol and thus does not create a salt, acid-base, or water problem). This form of therapy is superior to the administration of the sodium salt of ß–HB.

CASE 1–8:
SUICIDE ATTEMPT WITH INSULIN
(Case described on page 14)

(see facing page)

The excess of insulin causes:

- **Conversion of glucose by**

  Liver – to glycogen and conversion to fat.
  Muscle – to glycogen and for energy.

- **Uptake of fat by adipose tissue.**

  Deposition of circulating triglyceride.
  Inhibition of release of fatty acids from stores.

- **Uptake of amino acids by liver and muscle.**

- **Inhibition of synthesis of glucose by liver.**

  Amino acids are not available (less net protein breakdown).
  Glycerol is not available (release from adipose tissue is inhibited).

Thus, there are insufficient circulating fuels.

- The main problem is the brain, which requires 120 g glucose per day (there are no ketoacids as fatty acids are not being released from adipose tissue). The rest of the body also requires glucose. The other tissues must use glucose. Also, liver and muscle will store glucose as glycogen if these stores are not full. Hence therapy is to provide glucose orally or IV.

Priorities of Management

1. **Feed the brain 20 kcal/hr.** This means provide glucose (easy) or ketoacids (hard). Make the patient eat 5 g of glucose/hr. The problem is, other organs will oxidize or store some glucose.

2. **Provide sufficient glucose to fill stores:**
   - The major stores of glycogen are liver (100 g) and muscle (450 g).
   - The extra glucose needed depends on how full these stores were prior to therapy.
   - The other possible store, conversion of glucose to fat, is a slow pathway and will not use much glucose in 24 hr, but this rate increases with time.

3. **Provide glucose for ATP in other organs:**
   - The excess insulin means fat is not released from stores.
   - Other organs can oxidize 15–20 g of glucose per hour (60–80 kcal/hr).

CAUTION

Do not give too much glucose.

- If more glucose is infused than can be oxidized or stored, its concentration will rise in the blood and it will be excreted in the urine dragging out useful ions (sodium, potassium, chloride). (See chapter 4 for a discussion of osmotic diuresis).

INSULIN OVERDOSE

CASE 1–9:

1.

Very concentrated
solution

Therefore diminution of extracellular fluid and
blood volumes. Loss of water causes the volume
of cells to shrink.

H_2O from blood to intestine

2.

Rapid flow of glucose and nutrients (plus water) to blood.

Therefore, rapid increase in the concentration of
glucose and thereby, the release of insulin.

3.

Glycogen

liver

ATP

GLUCOSE

muscle
Glycogen
ATP

INSULIN

Rapid uptake of glucose by the liver and muscle
with excess insulin. Rapid uptake continues
beyond euglycemia, because insulin is still in
excess. Therefore hypoglycemia, with diminished
fuels for the brain, causes the brain to malfunction.

CASE 1–9:
DUMPING SYNDROME
(Case described on page 14)

(see facing page)

- Some patients after gastric surgery lose the reservoir function of the stomach; the stomach thus "dumps" its contents into the absorbing area (small intestine) too fast.
- This reservoir function prevents the signs of dumping.

> The rate of release of fuels from the stomach to the intestine approximates the rate of use of fuels at rest (2.5 kcal glucose/minute).

- Since contents of the stomach are very concentrated, slow delivery to the intestine limits movement of water from blood into the lumen of the intestines. Excess loss of water from blood causes a low circulating volume and ultimately, a poor supply of oxygen to tissues.
- The small intestine can absorb energy fuels very quickly. Thus the reservoir limits the rate of uptake of fuels into blood.

- Too rapid accumulation of glucose would cause hyperglycemia and glycosuria.
- Too rapid accumulation of amino acids can affect the brain, as some of these are neurotransmitters.
- Rapid hyperglycemia also causes excess release of insulin, which over–stimulates use of glucose, causing a later swing to hypoglycemia, and lack of fuel for brain.

The Symptoms

- Patients suffer initially from symptoms of water loss into the bowel – dizziness, nausea, sweating, light–headedness.
- Secondary symptoms relate to severe hyperglycemia, causing excess insulin production, and delayed hypoglycemia; this results in symptoms of sympathetic overdrive and insufficient ATP in brain (see Chapter 5 for more details).

DUMPING SYNDROME

BRIEF DISCUSSION OF CASES

CASE 1–10:
RAPID WEIGHT LOSS IN A CANCER VICTIM
(See page 27 for more discussion)

Margaret's weight loss was more than 0.5 lb/day. This could not be fat since she was inactive physically and had a modest caloric use. She had to be losing water. There was no excessive loss of sodium and water (ECF volume); hence she had to be burning lean body mass. Her problem was that the tumor's pyruvate dehydrogenase was very active, as this particular tumor could not burn fat (it lacks the enzyme to do so).

CASE 1–11:
NORMAL WEIGHT LOSS IN FASTING
(See page 28 and 29 for more discussion)

With no caloric intake, Henry must burn endogenous stores. Fat should provide most of his energy in the long run. However, the body switches from the fed state carbohydrate economy to the fasted state fat economy slowly. Hepatic glycogen lasts for 1 day and body fat takes over after 3–4 days. In the mean time, body protein is the main source of glucose for the brain and weight is lost at a more rapid rate.

CASE 1–12:
HYPOGLYCEMIA WITHOUT HYPOGLYCEMIA
(See page 30 for more discussion)

3.9 mmol glucose/l should be enough for the brain. The concentration of glucose might have fallen overnight. Her "panic attack" indicated that this just might have been the case. Where did the glucose come from to raise her blood levels to 4.5 mmol/l?

Sandy's "panic attack" may have promoted release of eprinephrine (adrenaline), which stimulated breakdown of glycogen and proteins in muscle, resulting in the formation of lactic acid and amino acids respectively, both of which were converted to glucose in the liver. It could also have broken down the small amount of glycogen remaining in the liver, releasing some more glucose directly to blood.

PART 4: METABOLIC PATHWAYS AND CONTROLS

CASE 1–10:
RAPID WEIGHT LOSS OF A CANCER VICTIM

> - Pyruvate dehydrogenase annihilates glucose and proteins!
> - The reaction catalyzed by PDH should be turned off whenever possible (by burning fat).

Margaret had an anaplastic (wildly growing) cancer. Her appetite was somewhat depressed. Despite a modest decrease in caloric intake, she lost 15 lbs in the past 3 weeks. She did not have a fever or excessive sweating, nor did she give a history of diuretic use, drug ingestion nor excessive activity. Her urine did not contain sugar or amino acids. What was her biochemical lesion?

CASE 1–11:
NORMAL WEIGHT LOSS IN STARVATION

> **THE FED STATE: A CARBOHYDRATE ECONOMY**
> **THE FASTED STATE: A FAT ECONOMY**
>
> - Without meals, burn fat and save glucose and protein.

Let's look at Henry (Case 1–6) again, but earlier in his life, when he realised he was not getting the jobs he wanted because he was overweight. At that point, he decided to stop eating. He only consumed vitamins, minerals and water.

How did his weight change with time?

What pathways and controls operate?

CASE 1–12:
HYPOGLYCEMIA WITHOUT HYPOGLYCEMIA!, THE REAL WORLD.

Sandy, a physician and research fellow, volunteered as a subject in a project on effects of fasting on nitrogen wastes. Coming in to work on the subway after 40 hr without food, she experienced a "panic attack" (classic signs of hypoglycemia effects on brain). The signs diminished such that she felt not too bad when her journey ended, despite not eating. At the lab, 1 hr after the attack, the concentration of glucose in her blood was 4.5 mmol/l whereas it had been 3.9 mmol/l the evening before. Explain.

NOTES ON SYSTEMS OF ENERGY METABOLISM

Some interconversions can occur in both directions, others only in one direction.

Two–way Streets

- All stores can be made from, and broken down to, their corresponding circulating fuels within the same system.
- All circulating fuels, except essential amino acids, can be made and broken down.
- Different pathways are used in each direction.

One–way Streets

- Pyruvate dehydrogenase (pyruvate to acetyl–CoA) and the ATP generation (acetyl–CoA to ATP) systems can only occur in humans and in other animals in the directions shown.
- Because some amino acids cannot be synthesized in the body, and all are needed to make protein, carbohydrate and fat cannot be made into proteins.

Inverconversion Between Fuels

- All fuels can make acetyl–CoA, and thus ATP.
- Fats can be made from carbohydrates and proteins.
- Carbohydrates can only be made from proteins.

Energy Balances

- Energy is involved in all these pathways.
- Making large chemicals out of smaller ones requires energy; all arrows pointing up in Figure 1–8 consume ATP.
- Outside the ATP generation system, only conversion of glucose to lactate releases ATP, and then only a little per glucose used (but this flux can be very rapid indeed).
- All pathways from circulating fuels to tissue intermediates are oxidations, releasing hydrogen as NADH, which is burned in the ATP generation system to give water and ATP.

PART 4. PATHWAYS AND CONTROLS

We present an overview of the pathways and their interactions.

METABOLIC PATHWAYS

> **The metabolic chart (Fig 1–8) shows that:**
> - All fuels feed into a single ATP generation system;
> - Only some fuels can be interconverted;
> - Control of PDH is the key to conserving glucose and protein.

Figure 1–8 shows how we view the pathways of energy metabolism.

FIGURE 1 – 8
SYSTEMS OF ENERGY METABOLISM

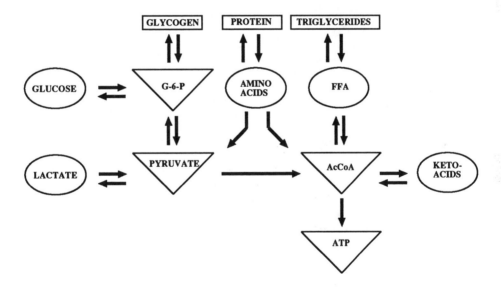

Legend: Energy stores are shown in rectangles, circulating fuels in ovals and the key tissue intermediates in triangles.

FIGURE 1–9
PATHWAYS AND ORGANS

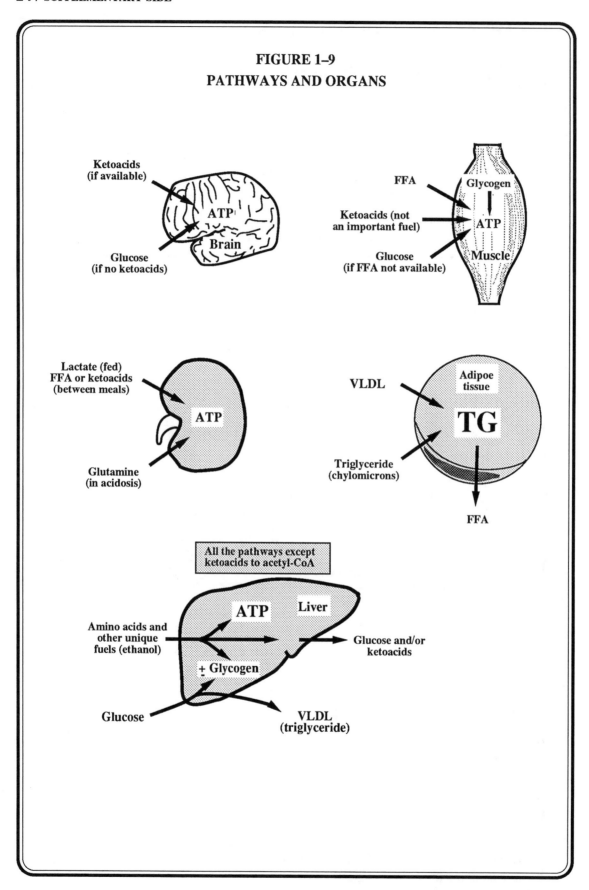

FUNCTION AND CONTROL IN SYSTEMS AND PROCESSES

> If you know the **FUNCTION**, you can deduce the **CONTROLS**

- The overall diagram in Fig 1–8 can be viewed either in terms of:
  - **SYSTEMS:** centred on types of fuel and pathways
  - **PROCESSES:** centred on functions of the body

FUNCTION	CONTROL
A. The Carbohydrate System:	
1. Glucose or glycogen to ATP	• Negative feedback by ATP and insufficient glucose.
2. Glucose to stores	
– glycogen	• Stimulated by surplus glucose, • Stops when store is full.
– triglyceride	• Stimulated by surplus glucose, • No limits.
3. Glucose precursors to glucose (lactate, amino acids)	• Supply of these precursors to liver.
B. The Fat System:	
1. Fat to ATP	• Stimulated by low glucose.
2. Fat to ketoacids (liver only)	• Stimulated by low glucose. • Limited by liver's need for ATP.
3. Fat transport from diet to store	• Stimulated by high insulin.
C. The Protein System:	
1. Protein to "stores" – protein first, glycogen next, then fat	• Stimulated by high glucose and high amino acids.
2. Protein to ATP	• Stimulated by high amino acids (diet). • Stimulated by low glucose (body).
D. Pyruvate Dehydrogenase:	
1. Glucose to ATP	• Surplus of glucose activates. • Feedback by ATP.
2. Glucose to fat (liver only)	• Surplus glucose overrides ATP control.
E. ATP Generating System:	
1. Final common path to ATP	• Control by ATP feedback.

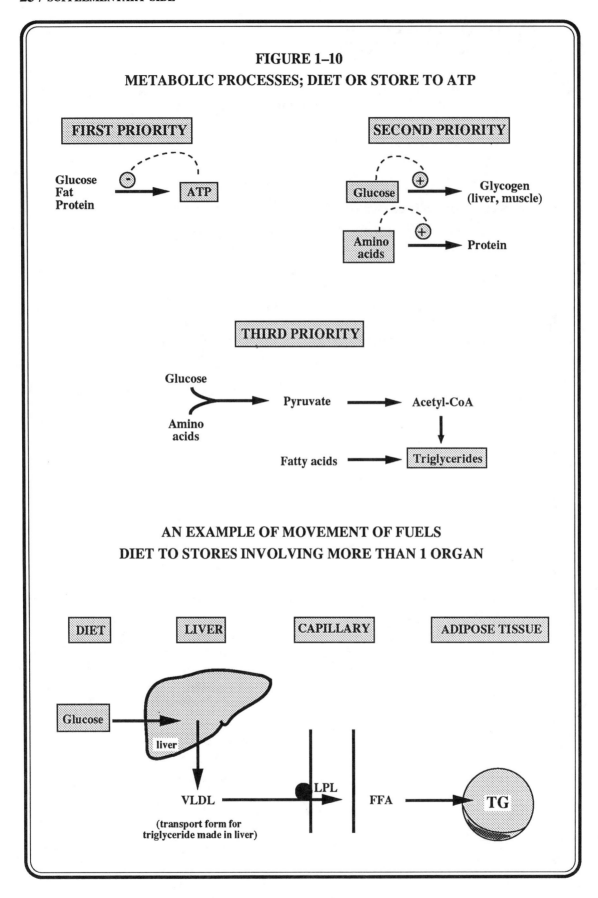

FIGURE 1–10
METABOLIC PROCESSES; DIET OR STORE TO ATP

FIRST PRIORITY

Glucose
Fat   ──────→ ATP
Protein

SECOND PRIORITY

Glucose ──(+)──→ Glycogen
                   (liver, muscle)

Amino   ──(+)──→ Protein
acids

THIRD PRIORITY

Glucose
          ⟩──────→ Pyruvate ──────→ Acetyl-CoA
Amino   │
acids   ↓
Fatty acids ──────→ Triglycerides

AN EXAMPLE OF MOVEMENT OF FUELS
DIET TO STORES INVOLVING MORE THAN 1 ORGAN

DIET   LIVER   CAPILLARY   ADIPOSE TISSUE

Glucose ──────→ liver

VLDL ──────→ ● LPL ────── FFA ──────→ TG

(transport form for
triglyceride made in liver)

METABOLIC PROCESSES

Metabolic Processes
- Begin with dietary or stored fuels
- End with stored fuels or ATP
- May involve more than one organ

- Metabolic processes deal with the whole body.
- They are defined by a specific metabolic function.
- We identify three groups of metabolic processes:

1. **From dietary or stored fuels to ATP:**
   - Supply of ATP for tissues is always the first priority for energy fuels.
   - Fuels stored in one tissue can provide ATP in another.

   The questions regarding control are:

   – How much should be used for ATP? Control is by product inhibition by ATP
   – Which fuels should be used? Controls preserve glucose and use fats

2. **From dietary fuels to energy stores:**
   (Fig 1–10)

   - First priority is to supply ATP for tissues.
   - Second priority is to replace protein and glycogen lost in a period between meals.
   - Third priority is to store excess as adipose tissue triglyceride.

   The question regarding control is

   – How much fuel to convert to which store?
   – Glycogen and protein stores increase in response to substrate supply, up to a limit determined by the size of these stores
   – Fat stores accumulate excess fuel without any limit

FIGURE 1–11
ENERGY TRANSFER PROCESSES

A) ATP SHUTTLE FROM LIVER TO THE RED BLOOD CELL

Although glucose recycles, it is really an ATP "shuttle" from liver to the red cells. This cycle is also called the Cori Cycle.

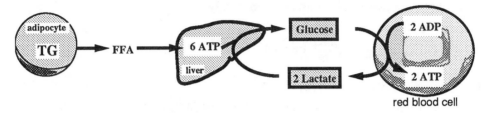

B) ATP SHUTTLE TO BRAIN: FAT STORY

Energy stored as fat cannot be used directly by the brain. Fatty acids are converted to ketoacids in the liver and this allows brain to use fat.

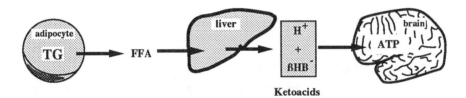

C) ATP SHUTTLE TO BRAIN: GLUCOSE STORY

When the concentration of glucose is low in the circulation, there is net breakdown of protein and glycogen in muscle. The amino acids and lactate released are delivered to the liver and made into the fuel for the brain, glucose.

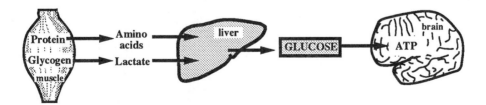

METABOLIC PROCESSES
(continued)

3. Energy transfer processes
(Fig 1–11)

In these processes a tissue converts one fuel to another for use by other tissues for the synthesis of ATP. Energy is used in one tissue to provide for another.

We identify 3 major examples:

A) The glucose–lactate–glucose cycle (the Cori Cycle);
red cell ATP comes from fat:

- Breakdown of glucose to lactate provides ATP (in red cells or anaerobic muscle).
- Lactate is reconverted to glucose (in liver) or glycogen (in aerobic muscle), consuming ATP.
- Note: breakdown of glucose to lactate yields $1/3$ of the ATP used in the synthesis of glucose from lactate. Hence the Cori Cycle consumes ATP which comes from the oxidation of fat.

B) Stored fat to brain ATP:

- Fatty acids are released from stored fat.
- Liver makes ketoacids from fatty acids
- Brain oxidizes ketoacids bodies to produce ATP (brain cannot oxidize fatty acids).

C) Muscle protein or glycogen to brain ATP:

- Exactly analogous to b); proteins or glycogen from muscle are released as amino acids and lactate respectively which are converted to glucose in the liver.

CASE 1–10:
CANCER CACHEXIA

- Low levels of glucose in the blood are likely between meals, as the tumor is burning glucose.
- Eating causes intermittently high insulin, so that ketoacids do not build up.
- Hence Margaret burns liver glycogen rapidly and relies on protein stores between meals.

NOTES ON PYRUVATE DEHYDROGENASE

> Turn off PDH between meals or
> "Burn fat and PDH is turned off".

- PDH destroys carbohydrates or their precursors because it catalyzes an irreversible reaction.
- Carbohydrates must be preserved for the brain. This occurs because the activity of PDH declines when fat is oxidized.
- PDH produces precursors of ATP, acetyl–CoA and NADH.
  - ATP, NADH and acetyl–CoA all are strong inhibitors of PDH.
- PDH produces the precursor of fat acetyl–CoA.
  - Feedback inhibition of PDH by its products can be overridden in liver by high levels of insulin.

CASE 1–10:
CANCER CACHEXIA
(Case described on page 22)

(see figure on facing page)

- Margaret's weight loss exceeds any reasonable expectation of burning too much fat, and no nutrients are being lost in the urine. Thus she must be burning "heavy" calories. This implies breakdown of protein.

- The tumor needs lots of energy, but cannot burn fat. Thus it consumes carbohydrate or carbohydrate precursors (proteins) from body stores.

- Pyruvate dehydrogenase in the tumor is always active which allows it to burn carbohydrate (and not fat). The reason PDH is always active is that the tumor cannot burn fat (which inactivates PDH).

Some questions to think about
(Chapter 9 provides food for thought)

1. In what metabolic situations might active pyruvate dehydrogenase be required? What tissues have these properties?

   a) All the time?

   b) Some of the time? When?

   c) Never?

2. If carbon from glucose must be conserved, especially in starvation, which is the most important point for control to be exerted at?

3. What types of control would you expect over PDH in the liver?

4. Look back over the previous cases. What were the roles of PDH in the various tissues in each case?

TABLE 1–7
DAILY WEIGHT LOSS DURING FASTING

This table shows theoretical loss in weight in g/day, resulting from fuels burned (and excretion of water for heavy calories).

FUEL STORES CONSUMED (g per day)

Energy Used (kcal/day)	Glycogen dry (g)	Glycogen wet (g)	Protein dry (g)	Protein wet (g)	Fat dry (g)	Fat wet (g)	Net Wt Loss (g/day)
CARBOHYDRATE STORE PHASE, DAY 1							
2200	100	400	50	200	215	215	815
PROTEIN USE PHASE, DAY 2							
1750	–	–	180	720	114	114	834
INTERIM–PHASE, DAYS 3 AND 4							
1500	–	–	15–150	60–600	140–150	140–150	200–750
KETOTIC–PHASE, DAYS 5– 50+							
1245	–	–	6	24	150	150	174
TERMINAL PHASE, DAY 50 OR MORE							
1000	–	–	250	1000	–	–	1000

CALCULATION OF FIGURES

The daily caloric consumption less the daily use of glucose by brain yields the amount of breakdown of fat needed. Breakdown of fat provides 10% of its weight as glucose (glycerol). The rest of the glucose must come from glycogen (day 1 only) or protein, of which only 60% yeilds glucose. Simultaneous equations for glucose requirements for the brain (g/day = 0.6 X amount of protein + 0.1 X amount of fat) and total calorie requirements (kcal/day = 4X amount of protein + 9 X amount of fat) provide the figures in the table.

CASE 1–11:
WEIGHT LOSS DURING STARVATION
(Case described on page 22)

> • The only good weight loss is the loss of fat!

Henry's use of fuels is governed by the following:

- His brain always requires glucose (5 g/hr unless ketoacids are high).
- His body's stores of glucose are limited; the only real store of glucose is glycogen in liver, about 100 g (20 hrs worth if used only by the brain).
- Fats from adipose tissue are the major store of energy.
- Fats cannot be made into glucose; (actually, the glycerol backbone of triglyceride, 6% of its carbon, can).

Hence, the supply of glucose for Henry's brain becomes a problem after glycogen in his liver has been used (in less than 1 day). The body resolves this problem in 2 ways:

- **Short term:** Liver makes glucose from amino acids from muscle protein.
- **Long term:** Liver provides ketoacids from fatty acids.
  - When the concentration of ketoacids rise to the 3–7 mmol/l range, these fat–derived fuels can replace about 80% of glucose oxidized by the brain.
  - Hence, there are 3 phases of normal fasting described on the following page.

Weight loss
(Table 1–7)

- Table 1–7 outlines the theoretical loss of weight during starvation.
- The high loss of weight in days 1 and 2 are due to the use of heavy calories; the small loss of weight in the ketotic phase of fasting reflects the use of the most efficient energy store, fat, or light calories.
- The requirement to use body protein in the period after glycogen in the liver is exhausted, but before ketoacids have built up, is the most damaging part of fasting.

Some Questions to think about

- In therapy, what would you recommend to Henry to add to his diet to minimize wasting of muscle?
- What will be the theoretical loss of carbohydrate, protein, fat and weight if Henry exercises each day, expending 1500 kcal per day (assume it all comes from fat)?

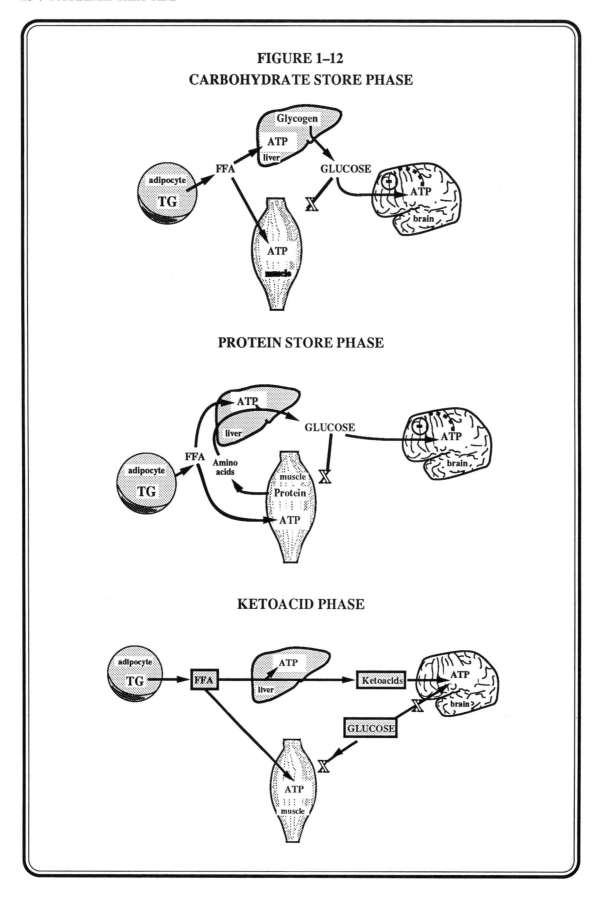

FIGURE 1–12
CARBOHYDRATE STORE PHASE

PROTEIN STORE PHASE

KETOACID PHASE

CASE 1–11
(Continued)

1. Carbohydrate Store Phase
(Fig 1–12)

This phase occurs between meals (see Case 1–6). Henry's normal energy use is 2200 kcal per day.

- The brain uses glucose obtained from liver glycogen until available stores are exhausted; up to 20 hrs at 5 g/hr.
- Fat stores in adipose tissue provide the energy needed by the rest of the body.

2. Protein Store Phase
(Fig 1–12)

This phase is bad news (see Cases 1–4 and 1–10). It is an interim phase, until the normal stable fasting phase.

Henry's energy use drops to about 1750 kcal because he feels poorly, and is no longer using the energy needed to inverconvert dietary fuels.

- The brain can use only glucose (because there are not yet enough ketoacids) and must get it all from protein (120 g glucose come from 200 g protein).
- Some glucose comes from the glycerol released from adipose tissue.
- Henry's energy use continues to drop a bit as he becomes more and more listless. However, ketoacids start to accumulate in his blood. His weight loss is interim between that for days 2 and 5.

3. Ketotic Phase
(Fig 1–12)

This is the stable phase of fasting.

Henry now has built up sufficient levels of ketoacids which can replace up to about 80% of the brain's need for glucose.

- Fat reserves meet almost all the body's needs for energy.
- Almost all the needs for glucose are derived from the glycerol part of the fat stores.

CONCENTRATION OF FUELS IN THE BLOOD (mmol/l)					
TIME DURING FAST (DAYS)					
	0	**1**	**2**	**3**	**21**
Glucose	5.0	4.0	3.6	3.3	4.2
Fatty acids	0.5	0.8	1.2	1.2	1.2
Ketoacids	0.01	0.05	1.2	3.0	6.0

CASE 1–12:
SANDY'S HYPOGLYCEMIC ATTACK:
FUEL FLOWS BETWEEN TISSUES

The other subjects would have been in the protein store phase of fasting (Fig 1–12). The 24 hr figures for Sandy showed a lower concentration of glucose and higher concentrations of ketoacids and fatty acids in the blood. After the attack, the concentration of glucose in her blood was similar to that in the volunteers, but ketoacids were very high.

DURING THE ATTACK

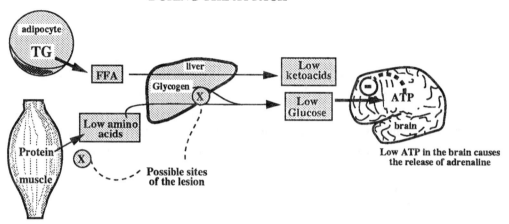

Low ATP in the brain causes
the release of adrenaline

AFTER THE ATTACK

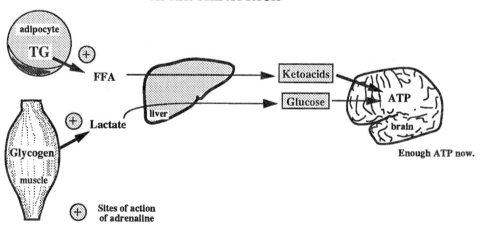

Enough ATP now.

CASE 1–12:
SANDY'S HYPOGLYCEMIC ATTACK
(Case described on page 22)

Of a number of volunteers, Sandy, was the only one who experienced these symptoms. Her figures for blood chemistry compared with the others in the study at 24 and 40 hours after starting the fast were:

Concentrations in blood mmol/l	Sandy		Others	
	24hr	40 hr (after attack)	24 hr	40 hr
Glucose	3.9	4.5	4.9	4.2
Ketoacids	0.6	4.0	0.15	0.8
Fatty acids	0.6	1.67	0.6	1.35

We assume that the panic attack occurred because her brain was not getting enough fuels, due to severe hypoglycemia. The level of glucose 1 hour after the attack was 4.5 mmol/l perhaps because adrenaline caused breakdown of glycogen in the liver and the muscle. Adrenaline could also have led to the higher levels of ketoacids after the panic reaction.

We can ask further questions.

1. Did she have high levels of ketoacids in the blood before the panic attack?

   Perhaps the ketoacid levels only rose during the panic reaction. The adrenaline released seemed to cause the very high FFA and even the low levels of insulin (see below). If the concentrations of ketoacids (and/or glucose) were really that high, she would not have had symptoms of lack of fuels in the brain.

2. Why did the normal concentration of glucose in her blood not cause a decrease in ketonemia?

   Perhaps the alpha–adrenergic reaction due to the low delivery of fuels to the brain prevented release of insulin; this, in conjunction with the high FFA, led to a high rate of production of ketoacids.

   Proposed sites of the lesion during the attack are shown on the facing page. Low levels of amino acids in the circulation favor the intrahepatic site but this must remain a speculation.

DISCUSSION

1. The absence of insulin:

The absence of insulin says **"let all stores pour out, without control"**. Glucose is released from glycogen in the liver, fatty acids are released from triglycerides in adipose tissue; amino acids are released from proteins and made into glucose, all at uncontrolled rates. The net result is very high concentrations of glucose, FFA and ketoacids in the blood.

The disease which causes low levels of insulin in the presence of its stimulator, high glucose, is **"Diabetes Mellitus"** (Chapter 4).

2. The major action of insulin:

The major action of insulin is to promote storage of fuels, and most importantly, to prevent the release of FFA from adipose tissue. This results in a low rate of oxidation of fat. Since ATP must be synthesized, this means rapid oxidation of glucose.

Given that a person at rest may oxidize 600 g of glucose (2400 kcal) per day and that the blood contains only 15 g of glucose, the patient will suffer from lack of glucose in 30 min. Since fat does not disappear instantly and there is some breakdown of glycogen in liver, the effect on the brain of the patient will occur after one hour (Chapter 6).

The tell-tale levels of circulating fuels from an overdose of insulin are low concentrations of glucose, FFA and ketoacids in the blood. The brain will suffer first as it has such a high metabolic rate and depends on glucose or ketoacids.

3. Dietary glucose and sodium:

The problem of lack of sodium is solved because of unique properties of the intestinal luminal membrane that permit almost unlimited absorption of glucose. Sodium that is absorbed with glucose escapes into the space between the cells and circles back to the unstirred layer of water at the luminal surface of the cell membrane to pick up another glucose molecule (Fig 1-13).

4. Cholera:

Patients with cholera secrete much salt and water into the GI tract. Secretion is stimulated by cholera toxin which permanently activates the synthesis of cyclic AMP in GI cells by modifying the transducer stimulatory G-protein (G_s) in the luminal membrane (see Chapter 7 for details).

Replacing the salt lost in cholera cannot be achieved simply by oral salt solutions; the salt is not absorbed rapidly enough without glucose. The oral treatment of cholera is a sodium and glucose solution because both are transported together through the transport system (Fig 1-13).

RECAP OF FUELS, ORGANS AND PATHWAYS

SOME QUESTIONS
(Discussion facing page)

1. What changes might you expect in the types of fuel oxidized and in the concentrations of key, circulating fuels if a person lacked insulin?
2. What changes would occur in the types of fuel oxidized in a patient who took too much insulin? How long will the patient remain conscious?
3. The daily intake of glucose is approximately 1,500 mmol; the total quantity of dietary sodium plus sodium secreted into the upper GI is about 600 mmol. How can the glucose be absorbed if glucose and sodium must be absorbed together?
4. How does knowledge of the glucose-sodium co-transporter help in design of therapy for patients with cholera?

FIGURE 1-13

MECHANISM FOR ABSORPTION OF ENERGY FUELS

The unique features are an unstirred layer and a tight junction between cells which is permeable to sodium but not chloride. This allows sodium to run in a circle in the micro-environment where glucose is absorbed; thus one sodium carries many molecules of glucose.

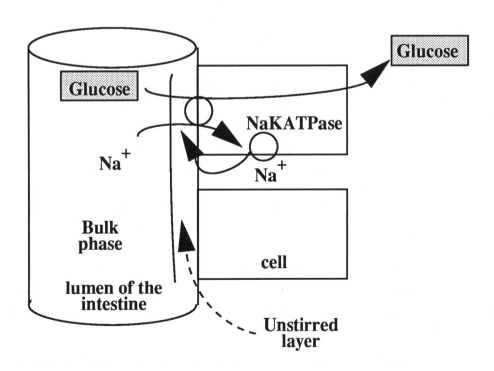

FLOW CHART 1–1

APPROACHES TO EVALUATE THE CAUSES OF ABNORMAL CONCENTRATION OF A METABOLITE

A) Metabolic process approach

The example is a high concentration of glucose. The key question is what can glucose be converted to, ultimately – stores or ATP?

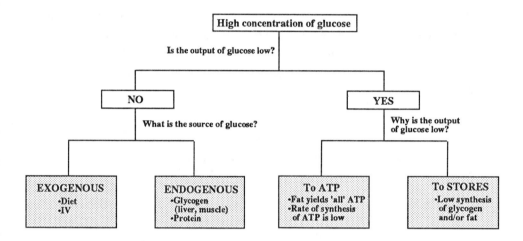

B) Function/Control Analysis

In this approach, we focus on what the primary role of the metabolite is and how its concentration is controlled normally.

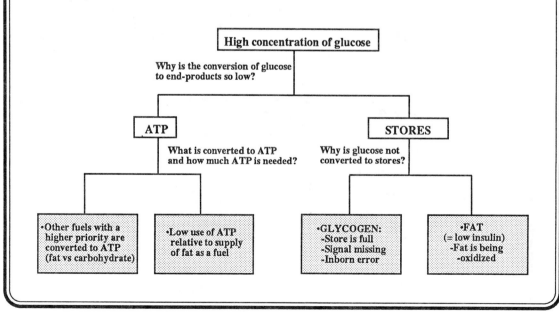

MORE ON THE EFFECTS OF INSULIN
Table 1-9

(see Chapters 8-12 for detailed mechanisms)

TABLE 1-9
PRINCIPAL EFFECTS OF INSULIN ON
CARBOHYDRATE METABOLISM

L = liver, M = muscle, B = brain, AT = adipose tissue

PROCESS	EFFECT	TISSUE	MECHANISM
Process 1: Increase removal of glucose			
A. Glucose to ATP	Increase	L	• Activate glycolysis via F2,6P2 • Activate PDH, both direct and via low availability of FFA
		M	• Low oxidation of FFA on PDH and glycolysis • Activate transport of glucose
		B	• Low availability of ketoacids
B Glucose to stores			
i) Glycogen	Increase	L	• Activate glycogen synthase
		M	• Activate glucose transport • Activate glycogen synthase
ii) Triglyceride	Increase	L	• Activate acetyl-CoA carboxylase • Inhibit oxidation of FFA • VLDL synthesis
		AT	• Activate lipoprotein lipase • Activate esterification?
Process 2: Decrease formation of glucose			
A. Glycogen to glucose	Decrease	L	• Inhibit phosphorylase
B. Glucongenesis	Decrease	M	• Inhibit net breakdown of protein
		L	• Activate PDH, PFK1, PK

FIGURE 1-14
USE OF CARBOHYDRATE FROM ONE MEAL

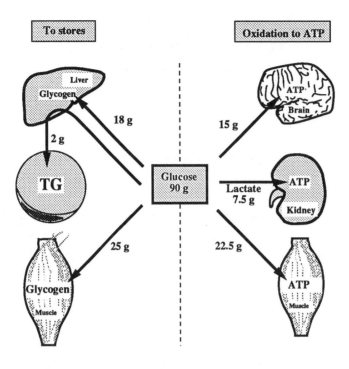

USE OF PROTEIN FROM ONE MEAL

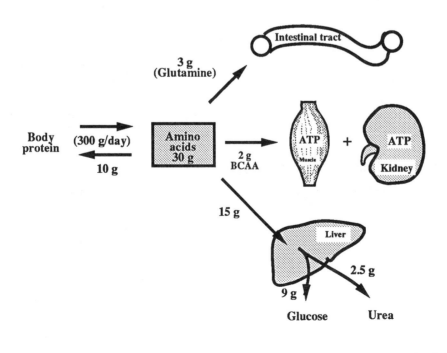

EMPHASIS ON QUANTITIES

FIGURE 1-14

DAILY FLOW OF BLOOD AND THE
CONSUMPTION OF OXYGEN IN ORGANS

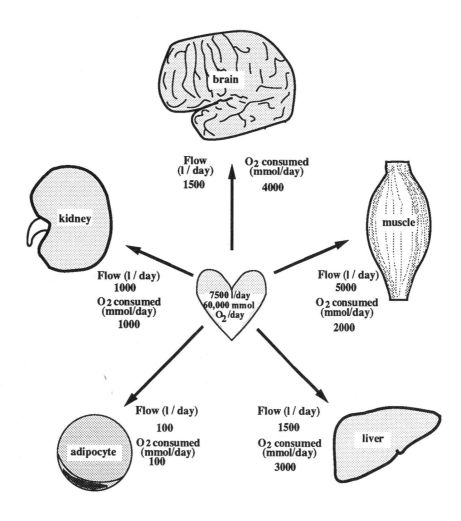

This Chapter introduces the ways in which the body keeps the pH of the blood constant.

- Acids (H⁺) produced in energy metabolism must be excreted by the kidney as ammonium.
- Ammonium is generated from glutamine.
- Protons are buffered in the blood by the the bicarbonate buffer system (BBS).
- The BBS is intimately linked to the transport of O_2 in blood.

NOTE:

In this chapter we introduce a shorthand notation for concentration, []. Thus [H$^+$] means the concentration of H$^+$.

FIGURE 2–1
OVERVIEW OF THE PRODUCTION OF WASTES

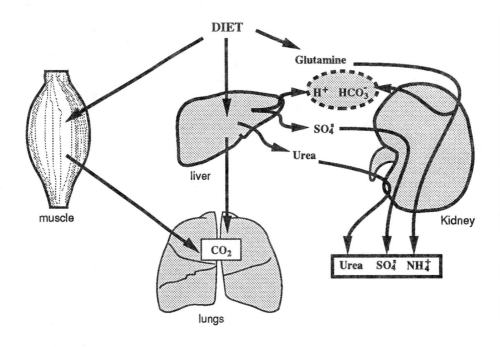

CHAPTER 2

METABOLIC WASTES

BRIEF DISCUSSION OF CASE 2–1:
SHIRLEY HAS KIDNEY DISEASE

- **Renal insufficiency causes inadequate excretion of:**
  - Sodium
    - Leads to hypertension.
  - Potassium
    - Leads to hyperkalemia, causing abnormalities of cardiac rhythm (arrhythmias) and poor function of the heart.
    - The most dangerous acute part of kidney disease.
  - Hydrogen ions (acid)
    - Leads to acidosis and contributes to death via hyperkalemia.

- **The aims of treatment are:**
  Minimize acidosis
  - Hydrogen ions come from:
    - Cationic (positively charged) and sulphur containing amino acids. Therefore reduce dietary intake of these amino acids. However, some are essential. Minimize breakdown of body protein.
  - Hydrogen ions can be removed during metabolism by:
    - Oxidizing anionic (negatively charged) intermediates.
    - These must be given with cations, such as sodium, which increase the sodium load.

- Minimize the intake of sodium and potassium
  - Foods to avoid:
    - Sodium–rich, such as sea foods, added salt.
    - Potassium, from cells (meat, broths, some vegetables).

- Diet should contain:
  - Calories for daily needs.
  - Essential materials – essential amino acids and fatty acids, vitamins, minerals.
  - Low amounts of the above potentially toxic materials.

CASE 2–1:
SHIRLEY HAS SERIOUS KIDNEY DISEASE

Shirley has very poor kidney function. She does not want to undergo treatment with an artificial kidney or receive a kidney transplant at this time. She feels reasonably well and her disease process is progressing slowly. Can you make suggestions as to how she should modify her diet to preserve lean body mass and avoid the accumulation of toxic materials?

OVERVIEW OF ACID–BASE BALANCE
(Figure 2–2)

- H^+ ions for excretion are produced in the liver.
- Production and excretion of H^+ ions are not synchronous events. Therefore H^+ ions, owing to their toxicity, must be buffered, temporarily. Only 1000 mmol of H^+ can be buffered.
- The H^+ are ultimately lost by being converted to water. CO_2 is the by-product, and it is excreted via the lungs. Bicarbonate is used up in the process.

$$H^+ + HCO_3^- \leftrightarrow H_2CO_3 \leftrightarrow H_2O + CO_2$$

- The kidneys generate "new" bicarbonate.

FIGURE 2–2
OVERVIEW OF ACID–BASE BALANCE

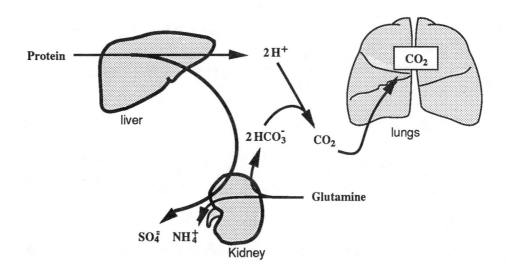

TABLE 2–1

FUELS IN A BALANCED DIET
(This table is largely repeated from Chapter 1)

FUELS	Amount (mol/day)	Weight g (g)	Energy (kcal)
Carbohydrate	1.5 (as glucose)	270	1080
Protein	1.0 (as amino acid)	100	400
Fat	0.36 (as fatty acid)	100	900
Oxygen	22	700	–
Total fuels (approx)	–	1170	2380

TABLE 2–2

SOURCES OF WASTES FROM DIETARY FUELS IN THE ADULT

The largest weight of daily waste is the CO_2 exhaled. Although tiny, excretion of NH_4^+ is very important for acid–base balance.

Type	FUEL g/day	CO_2	H_2O	UREA	NH_4^+
Carbohydrate	270	9000	9000	0	0
Fat	100	6400	6400	0	0
Protein	100	4000	4000	555	40

TABLE 2–3

RANGE OF [H+] SEEN IN CLINICAL CONDITIONS

CONDITION	$[H^+]$ nmol/l	pH	RANGE
ACIDOSIS	> 100	< 7.0	Life–threatening
	50–80	7.1–7.3	Clinically significant
NORMAL	40	7.4	Normal range
ALKALOSIS	25–30	7.4–7.6	Clinically significant
	< 20	> 7.7	Life–threatening

CLINICAL ASPECTS OF HANDLING WASTES FROM ENERGY METABOLISM

Most wastes are made into gases (CO_2) or water–soluble compounds (water, urea, ammonium) for easy disposal by lungs and kidney (Tables 2–1 and 2–2).

Hydrogen ions

- Although they form a tiny fraction of wastes (70 mmol of H^+ must be excreted per day), failure to excrete them can become life–threatening (Table 2–3).
- H^+ ions to be excreted are largely derived from oxidation of proteins.

Carbon

- Carbon in foods is converted to the volatile compound CO_2. CO_2 is excreted via the lungs in enormous amounts and without difficulty unless there is a serious lung problem.
- The CO_2 waste system is a critical buffer for H^+ in the body.
- The system to transport CO_2 in blood between tissues and lungs is intimately related to that for oxygen.
- Hemoglobin in blood plays a critical role in both the transport of O_2 and CO_2. CO_2 "speaks" via H^+ (high CO_2 = high $[H^+]$ = displaces O_2 from hemoglobin and vice versa).
- Thus adding O_2 to hemoglobin in the lungs aids in the removal of CO_2.
- Adding CO_2 in tissues aids the release of O_2 from hemoglobin near the tissues.

Nitrogen

- The principal nitrogen waste is urea. It is made in the liver. It removes the potentially toxic compound, ammonium (NH_4^+).
- The liver has an enormous capacity to convert NH_4^+ to urea, so this will only be compromised late in the course of liver disease.

CLINICALLY SIGNIFICANT ACID–BASE CHANGES

- Table 2–3 shows the clinically significant ranges of $[H^+]$.
- Thus a change in blood $[H^+]$ of 20–100 nmol/l can swing a person from life–threatening alkalosis to life–threatening acidosis.
- The different means of influencing blood $[H^+]$ are grouped clinically into acidosis (causing increased $[H^+]$) and alkalosis (causing decreased $[H^+]$). The causes for these can be either metabolic (acids other than carbonic acid) or respiratory (affecting carbonic acid directly).

Neutral Energy Fuels and Products

$$\text{Glucose} + O_2 \rightarrow CO_2 + H_2O$$
$$\text{Triglyceride} + O_2 \rightarrow CO_2 + H_2O$$
$$\text{Amino acids} + O_2 \rightarrow CO_2 + H_2O + \text{urea}$$

Most energy fuels:

Glucose, starches, triglycerides and 13 out of 20 amino acids are converted to CO_2, H_2O, urea, or neutral storage compounds (glycogen or triglyceride) without affecting H^+ balance.

Acid–producing Energy Fuels

$$\text{Methionine or Cysteine/cystine} \rightarrow SO_4^{=} + 2\,H^+$$
$$\text{Amino acid}^+ \rightarrow \text{Urea} + \text{Glucose} + CO_2 + H^+$$

The major examples are:

1. **Sulphur** in cysteine and methionine (uncharged amino acids) is excreted as sulphate ions (sulphuric acid).

2. Positively charged (**cationic**) amino acids (lysine, arginine, histidine) are excreted as urea, CO_2 and H_2O.

Acid–consuming Energy Fuels

$$\text{Amino acid}^- + H^+ \rightarrow \text{Urea} + \text{Glucose} + CO_2$$
$$\text{Citrate}^{-3} + 3\,H^+ \rightarrow \text{Glucose} + CO_2$$

The major examples are:

1. Negatively charged (**anionic**) amino acids (glutamic or aspartic acids) are excreted as CO_2, H_2O and urea.

2. The sodium or potassium salts of organic acids (citrate, malate) are excreted as CO_2 and H_2O.

ACID–BASE WASTES

Metabolism with No Acid–Base Implications
(see facing page for details)

- Most of energy metabolism has *no* acid–base implications because *neither* the major fuels *nor* the major products are anions nor cations.

Metabolic formation of acids and bases

> - Acids (H^+) are *produced* when fuels are converted to wastes with a more negative (or less positive) charge.
> - Acids (H^+) are *consumed* (base is produced) when fuels are converted to wastes with a less negative (more positive) charge.

- A small fraction of energy metabolism affects the concentration of H^+. It occurs when:
  1. **The total ionic charge on a waste product is different from the precursor fuel (see facing page).**
  2. **The charged metabolic intermediates, lactate and ketoacid anions accumulate.**
     - Lactic acidosis **(in hypoxia)**
     - Ketoacidosis **(in relative insulin deficiency)**
- In normal metabolism, more than 5000 mmol of lactic acid, fatty acids and ketoacids are produced and consumed per day. Since the rates of production and oxidation of these acids are equal, there is no acid load for excretion (Fig 2–3).

FIGURE 2–3
NET PRODUCTION OF ACIDS

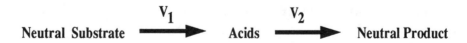

$$\text{Neutral Substrate} \xrightarrow{V_1} \text{Acids} \xrightarrow{V_2} \text{Neutral Product}$$

If $V_1 = V_2$, there is no accumulation of acid
If $V_1 > V_2$, acids accumulate (e.g. anaerobic muscle in severe exercise)
If $V_1 < V_2$, acids are consumed (e.g. recovery from lactic acidosis after severe exercise).

DISCUSSION OF CASE 2–2:
DIARRHEA
AFTER MILK PRODUCTS

- One possible diagnosis is a "nervous stomach" – anxiety surrounding the party. Possible, but a bit facile.
- Another possibility, food poisoning, is unlikely as no one else at the party had it.
- She could have had a toxin with a short life span. Such toxins (acids) can be made if food "stagnates" in the GI tract or if the bacterial flora is changed by antibiotics. She wasn't on antibiotics, so perhaps she did not absorb all her food properly.
- She drank milk. Many adults lose their ability to digest milk sugar (lactose) because low levels of the enzyme lactase in the small intestine mean that they cannot hydrolyze it. The toxins arise when the milk sugar reaches the large intestine (several hours after drinking milk), and this sugar is converted to a variety of organic acids by local, normal bacteria. These acids irritate the large intestine; they do not pose an acid base threat because the body can oxidize these organic acids to neutral end–products. The symptoms abate when milk sugar is no longer present in the large intestine.

FUTURE ADVICE

Explain the biochemistry of the disease to Mrs. Albright. Advise her to avoid ingesting large quantities of milk unless it is lactose–free and have other family members tested, as this low lactase may be a familial disorder.

DISCUSSION OF QUESTION 1

- Neutral fuels (muscle glycogen) can yield anionic intermediates (lactate$^-$) plus H^+ at life–threatening rates.
- Burning these lactate anions (or converting them to glycogen) forms neutral products and thus removes the H^+ load. Hence, there is no acid threat when H^+ are being consumed as fast as they are formed.

Conclusion

The net load of H^+ that requires buffering is much less than 1000 mmol.

CASE 2–2:
DIARRHEA AFTER MILK PRODUCTS

Mrs. Albright usually avoided milk. She hosted a birthday party for her 3 year old son and ate the same food as the others, milk, cake and ice–cream. Several hours later, she developed severe, crampy abdominal pain and explosive diarrhea. She feared food poisoning, but everybody else who attended the party felt perfectly well. Twenty four hours later, she felt fine. She did not take any medication at any time. What do you think was responsible for her symptoms? What advice would you give?

External Sources of Acids
and Bases
(see facing page)

The major sources are:

• Foodstuffs

– They normally constitute very minor acid or alkali loads.

• Digestion

– Secretion of acid into stomach does not cause an acid–base problem, unless the acid is lost via vomiting.
– Secretion of alkali into the intestines does not cause an acid–base problem, unless bicarbonate is lost via diarrhea.
– Bacteria in intestines may produce acids which cause two problems: an acid load and local irritation of the intestinal tract. This formation of acid rises if more fuel is delivered (e.g., failure to digest dietary carbohydrate or slower propulsion of food along the GI tract). In addition, a change in the normal bacterial content or composition may lead to overproduction of acids (e.g. after obstruction, blind loops of bowel or the use of antibiotics, see Case 2–2).

QUESTION
(Discussion on facing page)

1. A normal person can buffer 1000 mmol of H^+ and still survive. A greater load of H^+ is lethal. Why does an athlete who performs vigorous exercise survive a load of lactic acid which is >1000 mmol?

ACID–BASE ASPECTS OF KIDNEY FUNCTION

- The filtrate from the glomerulus has the same pH as blood (pH 7.4).
- To excrete the acid load produced by metabolism, the kidney must produce and excrete ammonium as described in Figure 2–4.
- The kidney filters a very large quantity of alkali in the form of bicarbonate (4500 mmol/day). This is reabsorbed primarily in the proximal tubule. By modifying the rate of reabsorption of bicarbonate, the kidney can excrete some alkali if it needs to.

TABLE 2–4
OVERALL SUMMARY OF ACID BASE BALANCE

1. **Diet yields H^+ load**

   Sulphur containing and cationic amino acids are present in larger amounts than anionic amino acids, and salts of other organic anions.

2. **H^+ consume bicarbonate**

   $$H^+ + HCO_3^- \rightarrow CO_2$$

   The $CO_2 + H_2O$ is lost via the lungs. This leaves a deficit of bicarbonate.

3. **Kidneys add "New" bicarbonate to the body**

   This requires conversion of glutamine to NH_4^+ plus HCO_3^- together with excretion of NH_4^+ in the urine, (Figure 2–4).

DISCUSSION OF QUESTION 2

Since the kidneys cannot make new bicarbonate, another process is required. Acetate (given as its sodium salt) can be used by the body as an energy fuel, removing H^+.

$$Acetate^- + H^+ \rightarrow 2\,CO_2 + 2\,H_2O + 10\,ATP$$
$$CO_2 + H_2O \rightarrow H^+ + HCO_3^-$$

$$Acetate^- \rightarrow CO_2 + H_2O + HCO_3^- + 10\,ATP$$

ROLE OF THE KIDNEY

> - Only the kidneys can excrete acid or alkali on a continuing basis.
> - The lungs can only help the $CO_2 - HCO_3^- - H^+$ equilibrium adjust to buffer a H^+ load; they cannot remove a continuing supply of H^+ because HCO_3^- must be replaced.
> - H^+ accummulation causes a deficit of bicarbonate.

- The kidneys control excretion of acid or base by adjusting the rates of excretion of NH_4^+ or HCO_3^-. Overall events are summarized in Table 2–4.
- The major excretion of acid by the kidney depends on conversion of glutamine to ammonium excreted and bicarbonate retained (Fig 2–4).

> Glutamine $\rightarrow$ $NH_4^+ + HCO_3^-$
> $NH_4^+ \rightarrow$ urine
> $HCO_3^- \rightarrow$ blood (removes H^+)

FIGURE 2–4
RENAL PROCESSES IN REMOVAL OF H^+

New bicarbonate (derived from glutamine) replaces the bicarbonate deficit.

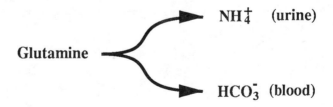

QUESTION
(Discussion on facing page)

2. In renal dialysis, the dialysis solution may contain an appreciable quantity of acetate. Why?

DISCUSSION OF CLINICAL EXAMPLES

1. The metabolic acidosis was due to 2 factors.

   a) The TPN solutions contained more sulphur containing amino acids than sodium or potassium salts of organic anions (glutamate, aspartate, citrate, malate, acetate and lactate). Hence there was net production of H^+.

   b) The kidneys could not metabolize glutamine (produce bicarbonate) owing to a primary kidney problem or a low level of glutamine in the plasma.

   What did the commercial companies do about it? They added sodium acetate to yield bicarbonate to "mop up" the H^+. It worked.

2. It is a net H^+ **removing** reaction rather than an H^+ producing reaction.

$$\text{2 Acetate}^- + \text{2 H}^+ \rightarrow \text{ß–hydroxybutyrate}^- + \text{H}^+$$

3 a.

   i) **Lactic acidosis:** A total oxygen consumption of 12 mmol/min is equivalent to 72 mmol/min ATP production (6 ATP per O_2). To achieve this synthesis of ATP in anoxia from conversion of glucose to lactate, production of hydrogen ion would need to be 72 mmol/min.

$$\text{Glucose} \rightarrow \text{2 Lactate} + \text{2 H}^+ + \text{2 ATP}$$

   Thus on average over the whole body, death from acidosis would occur in 7 min. However, the brain would die faster as it has a lower buffer capacity and a higher demand for ATP than the body as a whole.

   ii) **Ketoacidosis:** The production of ketoacids can be as high as 1 mmol/min. However, there is considerable oxidation of ketoacids. Thus the maximal <u>net</u> accumulation of ketoacids may be as high as 300 mmol per day; death will occur after several days.

   iii) **No kidneys:** Net production of acid is 70 mmol per day. Therefore, it would take more than 2 weeks to accumulate 1000 mmol H^+.

3 b)

   Importance of kidneys: The kidneys normally excrete 70 mmol H^+ per day, which can rise to 250 mmol in prolonged acidosis. The kidneys cannot help much in anoxic acidosis; the accumulation of H^+ is far too fast. They can help to a degree in diabetic ketoacidosis, but still get overwhelmed.

CLINICAL EXAMPLES
(see facing page for discussion)

The following questions illustrate how energy metabolism and acid–base balance are interrelated.

1. With the solutions originally used in total parenteral nutrition (TPN), patients developed metabolic acidosis. Why? What was done to avoid this problem?

2. During dialysis where acetate is a major anion, is the production of ß–hydroxybutyric acid a net H^+ producing or removing reaction?

3 a) How long will it take a patient to die of an acid load if there is:
    i)   Overproduction of lactic acid from total anoxia.
    ii) Diabetic ketoacidosis
    iii) No kidneys present.

    (Assume death occurs when 500 mmol of H^+ have accumulated acutely and 1000 mmol of H^+ are added on a chronic basis; total body oxygen consumption is 12 mmol/min; ketoacid production is 1 mmol/min; the daily net acid excretion by the kidneys is 70 mmol).

   b) From the examples above, how important are the kidneys for acid–base balance in diabetic ketoacidosis or in overproduction lactic acid due to hypoxia?

DISCUSSION OF CASE 2–3

- To function properly, Claude needs to produce 72 mmol ATP/min.
- The stoichiometry is:

| Fuel | O_2 used | CO_2 formed | ATP formed | O_2 used | CO_2 formed |
	(mmol/mol fuel)			(mmol/72 mol ATP)	
CHO	6	6	36	12	12
FAT	23.5	16	129	12.8	8.9

- Oxidation of carbohydrate produces more CO_2 per ATP than oxidation of fat. Thus Claude, with a problem in excreting CO_2, is best off burning fat rather than carbohydrate.

O_2 Consumption

- The oxidation of glucose rather than fat, to ATP consumes slightly less O_2 per unit ATP than does oxidation of fat. Therefore, if oxygen delivery is marginal, glucose is the more efficient fuel. However, there are other considerations:
  - Should the rate of turnover of energy rise, there will be a parallel rise in O_2 consumption and CO_2 production. Carbohydrate feeding can increase the rates of use of ATP in absorption and storage of glucose.
  - If biosynthesis of fat occurs, CO_2 is produced with little ATP (a rapid rate of fatty acid synthesis may occur during feeding of glucose).

DISCUSSION OF CASE 2–4
URSULA
PREPARES FOR THE SPRINT

- Blowing off CO_2 shifts the bicarbonate buffer equation to the right.

  $$H^+ + HCO_3^- \leftrightarrow H_2CO_3 \leftrightarrow CO_2 + H_2O$$

- Her blood becomes more alkaline.
- This lower $[H^+]$ causes H^+ to be released from other buffers (intracellular proteins).
- Lactic acid is produced in the sprint.
- Her hyperventilation has created extra parking spots for these H^+ (buffer them on intracellular proteins).
- She can overdo it; too high a pH is dangerous.

CASE 2–3:
FEEDING A PATIENT WITH SERIOUS LUNG DISEASE

Claude has smoked 2 packages of cigarettes per day for over 35 years. This smoking destroyed his lungs, leaving no pulmonary reserve. His major problem is that he needs to have a much higher than normal concentration of CO_2 in his blood to excrete all the CO_2 formed by metabolism each minute (12 mmol). Would it matter (with respect to the rate of production of CO_2) if he ate a carbohydrate–rich diet or a fat–only diet to synthesize all the ATP he needs each day?

* The first point to consider is whether removal of CO_2 or intake of O_2 is the more critical problem for Claude.

Hints for the Analysis

* A reasonable approach is to examine how much CO_2 is produced per ATP and how much O_2 is needed to yield a given quantity of ATP while oxidizing carbohydrate or fat.

* The excretion of CO_2 can be described as follows:

	Excretion of CO_2 (mmol/min)	=	Alveolar Ventilation (l/min)	X	[CO_2] mmol/l
Normal	12		5		2.4
Claude	12		2.5		4.8

Would you recommend the same diet if his problem was diminished availability of O_2 rather than elimination of CO_2?

CASE 2–4:
URSULA PREPARES FOR THE SPRINT

Ursula, a world–class sprinter, always prepares for the race in the same way. Just before the race, she is very "hyper". She overbreathes to get more oxygen into her lungs (or so she believes). Her trainer told her (correctly) that her blood was already saturated with oxygen and she could not derive further benefit from this overbreathing. Urusla knows that the overbreathing helps her acute endurance. She is correct. Why? Can she overdo it?

QUANTITY OF H⁺ BUFFERED BY THE BICARBONATE BUFFER SYSTEM (BBS)

- The **BBS** is the major H^+ buffer in the extracellular fluid (ECF). It can only accommodate a maximum of 360 mmol H^+ (equal to the total content of HCO_3^- in the ECF, 24 mmol/l X 15 l). At this point, the $[H^+]$ is about 100 nmol/l (pH 7.00).

- The BBS inside cells can accommodate a further 300 mmol of H^+.

- The normal dietary or metabolic acid load is 70 mmol H^+/day. The acid load can rise to 72 mmol of H^+ **per minute** in anoxia.

- Hence the BBS is only a temporary defence for an acid load; eventually H^+ must be excreted from the body for survival. A total H^+ load of >1000 mmol will lead to death (see Chapter 6 for details)..

FIGURE 2–5
DAILY TURNOVER OF H⁺

There are only minor fluctuations in the $[H^+]$ in the body.

Note the very large turnover of H^+ relative to the steady state concentration of $[H^+]$ in the body·

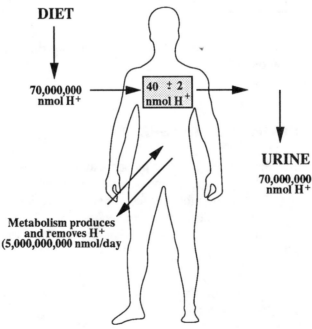

EXCRETION OF CARBON DIOXIDE

• Normally, 85% of the total CO_2 in blood is transported as bicarbonate ions and practically none as H_2CO_3.

   – Almost all CO_2 (>99.5%) is excreted via the lungs.

   – The transport of CO_2 in the blood provides major control benefits (explained later). It plays a critical role in the control of blood pH (hydrogen ion concentration).

Control of Blood pH
(see facing page)

• CO_2 is carried in the blood as a mixture of dissolved CO_2, carbonic acid and bicarbonate ions. The interrelations are shown in equation 1.

   – The enzyme carbonic anhydrase rapidly catalyses the interconversion of H_2CO_3 to CO_2 and water.

   – These reactions of the CO_2 system are always at chemical equilibrium; the concentrations of these chemicals always obey the formulae in equations 2 and 3 where Keq is the equilibrium constant.

   – Turnover of H^+ is illustrated in Fig 2–5.

$$H_2O + CO_2 \leftrightarrow H_2CO_3 \leftrightarrow H^+ + HCO_3 \qquad (1)$$

$$K_{eq} = [H_2O] \times [CO_2] / ([H^+] \times [HCO_3^-]) \qquad (2)$$

$$[H^+] = 23.9 \times PCO_2 / [HCO_3^-] \qquad (3)$$

Normal Values in Plasma

PCO_2 — 40 ± 2 mm Hg (SI units = 5.3 ± 0.3 kpascals)

$[HCO_3^-]$ — 24 ± 2 mmol/l

$[H^+]$ — 40 ± 2 nmol/l, pH 7.40 ± 0.02

23.9 — A composite constant which reflects the Keq, [H_2O], solubility factor for CO_2, different units (equation 3). This form of the equation is particularly helpful in clinical settings.

SOME QUANTITIES

O$_2$ SYSTEM
(see Lactic acidosis, Chapter 6, for details)

- Our typical person uses approximately 22 moles O_2/day (14 mmol/min)

- The concentration of hemoglobin (Hb) in blood is 140 g/l or about 2 mmol/l. Mol weight Hb = 66,000

- Each mol of Hb can carry 4 mols O_2; hence blood can carry 8 mmol O_2/l.

- Resting cardiac output is 5 l/min which carries 40 mmol O_2/min. Hence up to 30% (14/40) of the O_2 content is extracted.

- In vigorous long–term exercise, cardiac output and the extraction of O_2/l of blood increases to fulfill demand for oxygen (cardiac output = 20 l/min X 8 mmol O_2/l = 160 mmol O_2 delivery/min).

- Each O_2 can yield 6 ATP, therefore the maximum rate of turnover of ATP is close to 1000 mmol/min.

CO$_2$ SYSTEM

- Daily need for ATP requires the formation of 19 moles CO_2/day (13 mmol/min).

- Resting cardiac output is approximately 5 l/min. Hence each l of venous blood carries 2.6 mmol CO_2/min to the lungs for excretion, on top of the 24 mmol/l CO_2 + HCO_3^- normally present – almost a 10% turnover/min.

- In vigorous exercise:

  – Blood HCO_3^- decreases by >25% due to accumulation of lactic acid
  – Cardiac output increases 3–fold
  – CO_2 production increases 10–20 fold and the $[CO_2]$ in each l of venous blood rises about 10 mmol/l (largely as bicarbonate).

- Hence breathing rate and depth must increase markedly to achieve the needed 30–fold increase in the rate of alveolar ventilation, when there is no change in the P_{CO_2} of arterial blood.

Control of Rate of Breathing

- ATP requirements of the body determine the rates of both:
  - O_2 consumption (see facing page for more detail)
  - CO_2 production.
- The rate of excretion of CO_2 depends on how fast lung air is replaced by fresh air (which normally has a very low $[CO_2]$). Hence the need to excrete CO_2 determines the rate and depth of breathing.
- The blood PCO_2, via a change in the $[H^+]$ in cells of the brain, provides the signal for control over the rate of breathing.
  - A high PCO_2 raises the $[H^+]$ (lowers pH) (equation 1) and leads to an increase in the rate of breathing.
  - An artificially high rate of breathing (hyperventilation) lowers the $[CO_2]$, $[HCO_3^-]$ and $[H^+]$ (raises pH) in blood (called respiratory alkalosis see Case 2–4).
  - Two sites control the breathing rate:
    - A site in the brain primarily detects changes in the $[CO_2]$.
    - A site at the bifurcation of the major arteries primarily detects a lack of O_2.

The Bicarbonate Buffer System and O_2 Transport

- Oxygen (O_2) is carried in blood by being bound to hemoglobin (Hb).

$$Hb + 4\,O_2 \leftrightarrow Hb\,(O_2)_4$$

- $[H^+]$ greatly affects this reaction.
  - an increased $[H^+]$ pushes the equilibrium toward release of oxygen, and vice versa
- Since an increase in $[CO_2]$ increases $[H^+]$, a tissue producing CO_2 (burning O_2) will encourage blood to give up O_2 to the tissue.
- Removal of CO_2 from blood (in lungs) lowers the $[H^+]$ in the blood and thus encourages the transfer of O_2 into blood at the lungs (shifts equation to the right).

CASE 2–5:
WHERE IS HORACE'S MUSCLE GOING?

HYPOTHESES

- **Lean body mass is consumed to make glucose for the brain:**

  - If the stimulus to break down protein is the need for glucose, then the signal should be a low concentration of glucose in the blood. This was not the case in Horace. Hence, perhaps this was not the major reason for catabolism of protein.

- **Breakdown of lean body mass occurs to make glutamine to excrete NH_4^+:**

  - Ketoacidosis is a form of acidosis. In fasting, ketoacid anions appear in urine; hence NH_4^+ must be excreted in the urine to achieve acid–base and electrolyte balance.

  - Excretion of acid requires nitrogen (obtained from glutamine). Loss of nitrogen means a deficiency in amino acids and hence body proteins that were catabolized cannot be resynthesized.

  - Remaining amino acids thus go to the liver and are converted to glucose.

- **Testing these 2 Hypotheses:**

  - Give an oral load of alkali (sodium bicarbonate) equal to the rate of excretion of NH_4^+.

    - This will remove excess H^+ and thus reduce the need for nitrogen excretion.

    - Ketoacid anions can now be excreted as their sodium salts.

  - If the NH_4^+ option is true, total urinary nitrogen should decrease, both as NH_4^+ and as urea. This was observed; nitrogen excretion was halved.

  - Hence breakdown of protein in the ketotic phase of fasting seems to be increased by the need to excrete acid; the production of glucose can be viewed as a by-product at this stage of fasting.

CASE 2–5:
WHERE IS HORACE'S MUSCLE GOING?

> Control can change when function changes

Horace is extremely obese and is desperate to lose weight. He undergoes a complete starvation regimen (drinks water, has vitamin and mineral supplements). Weight loss is 300 g/day (see Case 1–11). We estimate that his energy consumption is 1500 kcal/day and he excretes 5 g nitrogen/day. If all the energy came from fat, weight loss would have been 150 g/day. Since protein is 1/6 N, 5 g N equals 30 g protein (120 kcal) or 150 g lean body mass (80 % water). Hence his weight loss is half fat and half lean body mass. During the fast, blood sugar was 3.3 mmol/l (60 mg/dl) in week 1 and 5 mmol/l (90 mg/dl) in week 4.

Why has lean body mass been catabolized in Horace? Consider whether this loss is to supply the brain with ATP (as glucose) or for acid–base considerations (to excrete NH_4^+)? How would you test these hypotheses?

BACKGROUND

- In chronic fasting, some breakdown of protein from lean body mass is required to supply the brain with glucose (via gluconeognesis, see Chapter 8 for details). The usual rate is 30 g protein/day.

- As ketosis of fasting develops, the brain can obtain energy from ketoacids. Now there is a need to excrete ketoacid anions with NH_4^+ (there are no other cations that can be spared and this promotes balance for bicarbonate). Half of the urinary nitrogen loss is as NH_4^+.

- The concentration of glucose in the blood rises progressively in this phase, hence there is already enough glucose for brain. Hence catabolism of protein is probably not required for glucose.

RENAL MEDULLA

• The medulla of the kidney has a poor and very discrete blood supply. Urea is trapped between the cells of the medulla, leading to a very high concentration of urea (and salt). When water must be retained, antidiuretic hormone causes the collecting duct membrane to become permeable to water. Water is then "sucked out of the lumen" by the concentrated urea + salt solution in the medullary interstitium.

HOW DO BEARS HIBERNATE?

• Peacefully – they do not pass urine.

• Urea, from breakdown of protein, enters the intestines. Bacteria in the early small intestine break the urea down and use the NH_4^+ to make amino acids, and thus proteins. These proteins are digested in the intestine; the amino acids are absorbed to resynthesize body protein. Hence CO_2 and water are the only wastes and both are excreted through the lungs (note the head down position, breathing through fur to minimize water loss).

GLOMERULAR FILTRATION RATE (GFR)

Each functional unit of the kidney is called a nephron. It filters plasma at the glomerulus. Since creatinine is freely filtered, not reabsorbed or secreted to any extent (little lie, there is some secretion), its rate of excretion can be used in conjunction with its concentration in plasma to calculate the GFR.

DISCUSSION OF QUESTION 3

When protein is broken down, almost all of the nitrogen is converted to urea. This urea either accumulates in the body or appears in the urine. When 1 pound of lean body mass is catabolized, 1/5 of that weight is protein (90 g, 80 % is water). Protein is 1/6 nitrogen; therefore, 15 g of urinary nitrogen (535 mmol urea) represents the loss of 1 lb (0.5 kg) of lean body mass . If there is no protein intake, this excretion represents loss of lean body mass.Brief discussion of events

NITROGEN EXCRETION
AS UREA
(see Chapter 12 for details)

- The vast majority (98%) of nitrogen from breakdown of protein is excreted as urea.
- Urea is not toxic or charged.
  - It is made almost exclusively in the liver.
- Nitrogen waste is carried to the liver as NH_4^+ and amino acids, mainly alanine and glutamine (the carbon of both of these amino acids is made into glucose).
- Synthesis of urea has notable properties:
  - The toxic product, NH_4^+ is removed.
  - Urea is synthesized at a very rapid rate by a pathway which has a 10–fold excess capacity.
  - The pathway of urea synthesis is closely linked to that of synthesis of glucose (the pathways share a common key intermediate (see Chapter 10 for details)).
- Urea crosses cell membranes rapidly.
  - In the kidney medulla, a high extracellular concentration of urea helps reabsorb water (see facing page).
- Urea appears in all body secretions:
  - e.g. 20–25% of the urea produced daily enters the intestines and is broken down to NH_4^+, which re–enters the blood and is converted back to urea in the liver. This is very useful for animals that hibernate (facing page).

Creatinine

- Creatinine, formed from muscle creatine phosphate (the ATP reservoir), makes up 1% of urinary nitrogen. Its measurement is valuable to clinicians to estimate a specific kidney function, the glomerular filtration rate (facing page).

QUESTION
(Discussion on facing page)

3. How might clinicians use the rate of excretion of urea to indicate whether a patient is losing too much muscle mass (i.e. is in a very catabolic state)?

Event 3–1: The 100 m Sprint

- The muscle can use glucose or glycogen without oxygen, converting them to lactic acid for production of ATP for short periods of time.
  - This pathway can produce ATP faster than complete oxidation of glucose to CO_2.
- The sprinter uses stored ATP (creatine–phosphate) for the first 3 sec, and then mainly anaerobic glycolysis.
- Production of lactic acid makes the concentration of H^+ in the muscle rise.
  - This limits the duration of the sprint.
- The coach might ensure that stores of glycogen in muscle are high.
- Rapid breathing before the race might help buffer the acid production (see Case 2–4, Ursula prepares for the sprint).

Event 3–2: The 1500 m

- The main fuel used is glycogen in muscle.
  - This must be burned to CO_2 to minimize the build–up of lactic acid.
- Maximal speed will be limited by delivery of O_2 to muscle, and efficiency of its use for the synthesis of ATP.
- Fuel intake should aim to preserve glycogen in muscle.

Event 3–3: The Marathon

- Fats are significant fuels in the marathon, but the rate of synthesis of ATP is not as fast from the oxidation of fat as it is from the oxidation of glucose.
- Eating glucose during the race does not help much, as it is released only slowly from the stomach into the intestine.

CHAPTER 3

ENERGY METABOLISM IN MUSCLE

- Skeletal muscle can vary its rate of use of ATP over a 20–fold range.
  - This places demands on the other organs of the body.
- Chapter 3 examines 3 races, the 100 m dash, the 1500 m and the marathon events.
  - For each race, the same general questions can be asked:
    - What fuels are used by the muscle?
    - What limits the maximal speed that can be achieved?
    - How can modification of fuel intake affect performance?
- Specific questions can also be asked for each event.

Event 3–1: The 100 m Sprint

- Sharon is an honest coach who uses legal means only.
  - Can you help her with the above questions?
  - Will rapid breathing before the race help improve the performance of her athletes?

Event 3–2: The 1500 m

- In addition to the general questions:
  - Why is the average speed less in this race than for a sprint?
  - What fuels are used during the race and for the finishing 'kick'?
  - What is the metabolic problem with starting the finishing 'kick' too early?

Event 3–3: The Marathon

- In addition to the general questions:
  - Why is the average speed slower in this race than the 1500 m?
  - Can the runner of the marathon race eat glucose fast enough to provide energy for muscles?
  - Are there controls which prevent muscle from consuming fuels needed by the brain?

Further Questions

What steps might an ambitious and somewhat amoral coach use to help his or her athletes (see page 48)?

Coordination of Heart and lungs During Exercise

- The capacity of the blood to carry oxygen exactly matches the quantity of oxygen in the air breathed at rest.
  - Cardiac output and alveolar ventilation (delivery of air) are both 5 liters/min.
  - Air and blood each contain close to 8 mmol O_2 per liter.
- Alveolar air contains about 4 x more O_2 than CO_2 per liter.
  - 2 mmol CO_2/liter of alveolar air (at 40 mm Hg).
- When carbohydrate is oxidized, O_2 is converted to CO_2, 1:1.
  - Glucose + 6 O_2 $\rightarrow$ 6 CO_2 + 6 H_2O + 36 ATP

- **Conclusion**
  - If all the O_2 is used from a liter of blood (producing 8 mmol of CO_2/liter), the alveolar ventilation must be 4 x the cardiac output to eliminate that CO_2 without a rise in its concentration.
  - Corollary: Rapid breathing is primarily to rid the body of CO_2 during severe exercise.

Training of Athletes Has a Number of Effects

- **Heart**
  - An increase in cardiac output results from:
    - Increased cardiac stroke volume.
    - Decreased resting cardiac rate.

- **Skeletal Muscle**
  - A grater capacity for synthesis of ATPis caused by:
    - Increased supply of blood to muscle cells (more of the small blood vessels called capillaries).
    - Increased amounts of glycogen.
    - Increased amount of enzymes in muscle which oxidize fuels (TCA cycle enzymes).
    - Increased myoglobin to help delivery of O_2 to mitochondria.

MUSCLES

> - Muscle is not a homogeneous organ.
> - Heart and lungs work in a synchronous way to deliver O_2 and remove CO_2.

- The two major organs grouped under the category of muscle are:

1. Heart:

- Always requires oxygen.
- Can increase its rate of production of ATP approximately 4–fold.
- Cardiac output can rise 4–5–fold to deliver up to 170 mmol O_2/min.
- Training increases performance.

2. Skeletal Muscle:

- Can operate with or without oxygen.
- At rest, it uses 25% of the daily consumption of O_2.
- Has a huge energy reserve (450 g of glycogen).
- Can increase its consumption of oxygen 20–fold (to 160 mmol/min).
- Can buffer H^+ more effectively than other organs.
- Training increases performance.

Fibre Types in Skeletal Muscle:

- Fast–twitch fibres for a sprint:
  - White muscle mainly.
  - Rich in creatine–phosphate, which acts as a reserve fuel (and buffer).
  - High glycolytic rate, low oxidative rate.
  - Relatively poor blood supply, few mitochondria, little myoglobin or TCA cycle enzymes (see facing page for details).
- Slow–twitch fibres for endurance:
  - Red muscle.
  - Depends on supply of oxygen and the ATP generation system.
    - Therefore has many mitochondria and much myoglobin.

TABLE 3–1
TURNOVER OF ATP IN MUSCLE

ATP Source	Quantity	Speed	Comments
ATP itself	• very small		• Lasts 1 second
Creatine Phosphate (Cr–P)	• Small (25 mmol/kg)	• Fastest precursor of ATP • Equilibrium reaction	• Lasts 3 seconds in a sprint • Supplies H^+ buffer (P_i) • 1 ATP/Cr–P
Anaerobic Glycolysis	• Large pool of glycogen (450 g)	• Fast pathway	• Lasts minutes • Leaves H^+ load • 1 ATP/H^+
Aerobic Glycolysis	• Muscle glycogen (450 g) • Liver glycogen (100 g) • Dietary glucose	• Moderate speed of formation of ATP • Limiting step is entry of pyruvate into mitochondria.	• Lasts 1–2 hours • Makes 36 ATP per glucose or 38 ATP per glucose of muscle glycogen.
Oxidation of FFA	• Very large store of fat in adipose tissue, small store of fat in muscle.	• Slowest rate of synthesis of ATP. • Limit is diffusion of FFA from blood.	• Lasts very long time. • Less ATP/O_2 than glucose • Mitochondria–rich muscles only (slow–twitch fibres).

SOME PROCEDURES ARE OFTEN SUGGESTED TO HELP ATHLETIC PERFORMANCE

Blood Doping

- Injection of concentrated red cells collected weeks earlier from the runner, or stimulation of the production of red cells by erythropoietin, to increase the content of oxygen in blood.
  - It is not expected to help a sprinter.
  - The dangers are that it causes the viscosity of blood to rise (hence a fall in cardiac output). Also, a higher PCO_2 in venous blood and muscle may limit performance.
  - There is a delicate balance between gain or loss of performance.
  - The real benefit is, at best, very slight (but may be enough to win the gold medal).
  - Another major benefit may be psychological.

Stripping (Vigorous Exercise Several Days Before) and Supercompensation

- Consuming carbohydrate–rich meals after depletion of glycogen in muscle can increase stores of glycogen in muscle considerably.
- This is likely to be useful in marathon races, when glycogen in muscle becomes limiting.

Soda Doping

- Consume considerable sodium bicarbonate to prepare for the acid load (lactic acid).
- Some athletes do show improved performance over short distances, but probably not for the reason expected. We suspect that an increase in cardiac output due to the sodium load was more important than the influence of bicarbonate *per se*.
  - Not enough bicarbonate is added to make a significant difference.
- The downside risks include a paradoxical loss of ECF volume due to a shift of water into the intestines before the $NaHCO_3$ is absorbed.
- In addition, the extra bicarbonate will be converted to CO_2 and the lungs are already near their limit to remove CO_2 without a rise in its concentration.
- An increase in urine volume might not help in a marathon with lots of spectators.

The H+ Story of the Sprint

- **Formation of H+**

  - Formed during glycolysis from glycogen

    $$Glycogen \rightarrow 2\,H^+ + 2\,Lactate^- + 3\,ATP$$

- **Buffering of H+**

  - The breakdown of creatine–phosphate to creatine and inorganic phosphate consumes one H^+ per molecule.
  - This can absorb 14 mmol H^+/kg muscle.
  - Histidine, an amino acid in proteins and special dipeptides in muscle (carnosine and anserine) can buffer about 20 mmol H^+/kg muscle with a decline in pH from 7.4 to 6.8.

- **Balance of H+**

  - If 20 mmol H^+ are buffered on histidine, and 14 are removed through breakdown of Cr–P, conversion of glycogen to lactic acid would have produced 34 mmol H^+. Since 2 H^+ produced per 3 ATP formed, glycogen yielded close to 50 mmol ATP and provided close to 75% of the ATP expended in the race.

- **Fatigue might result from a low pH due to:**

  - A decreased rate of synthesis of ATP secondary to inhibition of glycolysis by H^+.
    - However, the decline in the concentration of ATP in muscle is only modest.
  - A decreased release of Ca^{++} from sarcoplasmic reticulum secondary to its enhanced binding at a low pH.
  - Interference with interactions between actin and myosin, the contractile elements.

Discussion of Question

- Glycogen $\rightarrow$ 3 ATP + 2 H^+ per glucose used.
- If the Vmax was 2 mmol/min/kg.
  - In 10 seconds, 20 mmol of glucose will yield 60 mmol of ATP.
- The yield of ATP needed from glycolysis is 50 mmol/10 sec, see above.

Conclusion

The data are internally consistent if this enzyme is fully activated very quickly.

SITUATION 3–1:
THE 100 METER SPRINT IN MORE DETAIL

• **During the race:**
  – No need for O_2.
  – Uses energy at absolutely maximal rates (200 kcal/10 sec).
  – Average speed 10 m/sec.
  – Uses fast–twitch fibres.
  – ATP from creatine–phosphate (3 sec) and from glycolysis (7 sec).
  – Cost is production of H^+ (**see facing page**).
    – Build up of H^+ limits duration to about 20 sec.
    – The pH of muscle can fall to 6.4.

• **Typical quantities associated with 10 second sprint:**
  – Rate of turnover of ATP = 50 mmol/kg muscle/10 sec.
    – 14 mmol from creatine–phosphate/kg muscle.
    – 36 mmol from glycolysis/kg muscle.

• **After the race:**
  The large amount of lactic acid produced during the race must be consumed.
  – Some is used in muscle:
    – Reconverted to glycogen.
    – Burned to CO_2 to provide ATP.
  – Most of the rest is converted to glucose or glycogen in liver.
  – Some more is consumed in kidney and other organs, to provide ATP.

QUESTION
(Discussion on facing page)

A leading investigator measured the activity of one of the glycolytic enzymes (phosphofructokinase–1). He stated that the maximal activity was 2 mmol/min/kg of muscle at 37° C. Could this measurement be correct?

O_2 and CO_2 in Exercising Muscle

- If muscle uses all the O_2 which the blood supplies, the blood must carry away close to 8 mmol/l CO_2 (if glucose is the fuel).
- CO_2 is transported as $H^+ + HCO_3^-$ (see Chapter 2).
- The H^+ must be buffered by proteins in blood {mainly hemoglobin (Hgb)}.
- H^+ and O_2 compete for binding to Hgb.
  - Hence high CO_2 in muscle aids in displacing O_2 from Hgb.
  - Low CO_2 in lungs aids binding of O_2 to Hgb.
- Content of Hgb in blood (140 g Hgb/l) can bind 3.5 mmol H^+/0.1 pH unit fall.
  - Hence a fall of almost 0.3 pH units is needed to carry 8 mmol CO_2/l.
  - This fall in pH is equivalent to a doubling of the concentration of H^+.
  - To maintain equilibrium in the Henderson equation (see Chapter 2), the P_{CO_2} must also double (approximately) to 80–90 mm Hg.

Conclusion

- Extracting all the O_2 from blood yields a very high concentration of CO_2 in muscle, and thereby, a lower pH in muscle.

TABLE 3–2

FUELS USED IN A MARATHON RUN

Data were obtained from American Journal of Physiology 108:203, 1934. Carbohydrate is used earlier and fat later at a constant rate of consumption of oxygen. Hypoglycemia develops later in the race.

Time Period	O_2 Consumed	ATP Produced	Source ATP		[Glucose] Blood
			Glucose	Fat	
(min)	(mol/hr)	(mol)	(mol)		(mmol/l)
0–60	10.1	62	50	11.8	5.6
60–120	10.4	61	25.7	36.7	4.6
120–180	10.7	62	20.5	40.5	3.8
End (total)	31.2	185	96.2	88	

SITUATION 3–2:
THE 4 MINUTE MILE IN MORE DETAIL

- Average speed is 6 m/sec.
- ATP is produced mainly from metabolism of glycogen in muscle and of some glucose from the circulation (also glycogen in liver).
- Fat is not an important fuel for this race.
- Oxygen is a key metabolite; CO_2 is a product (1:1 with O_2).
- The rate of production of ATP is limited by the rate of entry of pyruvate into mitochondria.

- **Quantities in 1 liter of blood**
  - 8 mmol of O_2.
  - 5 mmol of glucose.
    Since only 1.3 mmol of glucose can be burnt with 8 mmol of O_2
    (Glucose + 6 O_2 $\rightarrow$ 6 CO_2), the supply of glucose is not limiting.
  - Muscle can receive up to 160 mmol of O_2/min; this could oxidize 27.5 mmol of glucose/min (5.4 g of glucose/min)!

EVENT 3–3:
THE MARATHON IN MORE DETAIL

- Average speed is 4.2 m/sec.
- About 10 mol O_2 are consumed/hr, equivalent to 1.67 mol or 240 g glucose/h.
- A 2.2 hr race thus could consume more glucose than the body contains.
- Glucose must be preserved for brain.
- Hence fat must be used.
  - Fat takes over from glucose (glycogen) as the dominant fuel as the race progresses (Table 3–2).
  - Use of glucose for energy in muscle causes progressive loss of glycogen from liver and muscle, and a lowered concentration of glucose in the blood.
  - Concentrations of fatty acid in blood increase as a result of the lower concentration of glucose.
  - Hence, the rate of oxidation of fatty acids can increase.
  - Ketoacids do not accumulate significantly, owing to short time period and the high rate of use of fuels.
- Importance of slow twitch fibres.

DISCUSSION

1. Products of Metabolism in Muscle; "hit the WALL"

a) H^+ are produced at close to 2 mmol/kg of muscle per second. Since 1 kg of muscle can buffer up to 40 mmol H^+ and still function well, production of H^+ can be tolerated at this rate for a maximum of 20 seconds. When more H^+ accumulate, the rate of production of ATP declines and the runner slows down.

b) CO_2: If muscle extracts 100% of O_2 from each liter of blood delivered to it, it must transport 8 mmol of CO_2 away (RQ is 1). To do this, the P_{CO_2} would be close to 80 mm Hg. This requires an even higher PCO_2 in muscle cells and an intracellular fluid pH to fall by at least 0.3 units (every doubling of P_{CO_2} cause the pH to fall 0.3 units). These changes are still compatible with high performance. If CO_2 is also produced by anaerobic acid production, the P_{CO_2} will rise even further and compromise muscle performance ("hit the wall").

2. High Rate of Synthesis of ATP at a Low P_{O_2}

Diffusion of O_2 will be faster if the P_{O_2} in mitochondria of muscle is very low. Thus the objective is to keep a low P_{O_2} in mitochondria of muscle.

• To obtain maximum flux in the equation at equilibrium, the product of the concentration of reactants must exceed that of the products of that reaction.

• Accordingly, if the concentration of one of the reactants must decline (P_{O_2}), there must be a larger rise in the concentration of the other reactants.

• Because of the controls of the pathway to generate NADH (the citric acid cycle). a very high concentration of NADH occurs when there is a small decline in the concentration of ADP. The net result is a displacement to the right of the equilibrium reaction shown on the facing page

3. Provision of Glucose to Muscle During a Marathon Race

– Demand for oxygen is 10 moles O_2 per hour. This is equivalent to 240 g of glucose/hour (total store of glucose is about 600 g). Therefore, there is not enough glucose in the body for a 3 hour race.

– The gastrointestinal tract can only supply glucose at a rate which matches body needs at rest (close to 30 g of glucose/hour); this minimizes the risk of hyperglycemia. The rate–limiting step is the rate of emptying of the stomach. Thus only 10% of need during the marathon can be met by the gastrointestinal tract.

QUESTION

(Discussion on facing page)

1. What is meant by "hitting the wall" in a race?

---

2. What are the biochemical adaptations that improve the ability of muscle to extract oxygen from the circulation?

Hints

- Consider the pathway for the synthesis of ATP as an equilibrium equation.

  NADH (from the oxidation of fuels in the TCAC) $+ \, \mathbf{O_2} + \mathbf{ADP} + \mathbf{P_i} \leftrightarrow \mathbf{ATP}$

- The system is designed to flow rapidly at the lowest concentration of O_2 to yield the highest concentration of ATP.

---

3. How much glucose can be provided to muscles during the marathon?

TABLE 4–2
MAIN TYPES OF DIABETES MELLITUS

Disease Classification	Distinguishing Features
• Type I; insulin dependent diabetes mellitus (IDDM)	• Usually thin; • Under 40 at onset; • Onset is acute or subacute; • Prone to ketoacidosis; • Requires insulin to maintain life.
• Type II; non–insulin dependent diabetes ellitus (NIDDM)	• Generally obese; • Over 40 at diagnosis; • Gradual onset; • Rarely ketotic; • Family history positive; • May not need insulin unless very strict control is desired.
• Pancreatic destruction (e.g. pancreatitis)	• Underlying disease
• ß–cell suppression (low insulin, but not really diabetes mellitus).	Alpha–adrenergics (eg –from a low ECF volume), phaeochromocytoma, • Drugs (e.g. dilantin, diuretics) • Certain endocrinopathies.

CHAPTER 4

DIABETES MELLITUS

KEY POINTS CONCERNING
ENERGY METABOLISM
IN DIABETES MELLITUS

• The normal concentrations of glucose in blood are shown in Table 4–1.

TABLE 4–1
NORMAL CONCENTRATION OF GLUCOSE IN BLOOD

	mmol/l	mg/dl
Before eating meal	3–4	55–70
Maximum while eating	7–8	130–150
2–3 hrs after absorption	3–5	55–90

• **Diabetes Mellitus** is a symptom complex caused by a relative lack of the metabolic actions of insulin (there is also a role for elevated concentrations of counter–regulatory hormones such as glucagon). The first sign is often hyperglycemia.

• The biochemical basis for hyperglycemia in diabetes mellitus is that glucose input into the circulation continues while its oxidation and/or conversion to stores are markedly impaired.

• The major mechanism whereby insulin accelerates the oxidation of glucose is by decreasing the rate of mobilization of fat stores, and thus preventing the oxidation of fat.

• Ketoacidosis, very high concentrations of ß–hydroxybutyric and acetoacetic acids, results from a complete lack of insulin. Ketoacidosis is prominent only in the end–stages of insulin lack and is much more prominent in insulin–dependent diabetes mellitus type 1.

• The clinical spectrum of diabetes mellitus is shown in Table 4–2.

• Some of the complications of diabetes mellitus appear to be secondary to hyperglycemia (page 58).

DISCUSSION OF CASE 4–1: AUNT AGNES HAS DIABETES IN POOR CONTROL

Hyperglycemia results from increased input of glucose to blood and/or decreased utilization of glucose.

1. INCREASED INPUT OF GLUCOSE

> Any input of glucose is too much in diabetes mellitus in poor control.

- Diet:
  - Because she was thirsty, Agnes drank several liters of apple juice (750 mmol glucose/l).
- Glycogen:
  - Glycogen in liver breaks down to yield glucose, until this store is depleted (<500 mmol).
  - Low insulin/high glucagon stimulates breakdown of glycogen in liver.
  - Muscle does not break down glycogen to glucose as enzyme is lacking.
- Protein to glucose; a 2 step control
  - Low insulin/high glucagon accelerated net breakdown of protein, largely in muscle owing to its mass (can yield about 400 mmol glucose/day).
  - The amino acids released are converted to glucose in her liver (gluconeogenesis).

2. DECREASED UTILIZATION OF GLUCOSE

> Key control by insulin is over release of fat stores.

- Glucose to ATP + CO_2 is low
  - **Muscle, Kidney:** Oxidation of fatty acids prevents oxidation of glucose.
  - **Brain:** Ketoacids must be oxidized to limit use of glucose. The key sites of regulation are pyruvate dehydrogenase and phosphofructokinase–1 in glycolysis. Brain can oxidize 670 mmol of glucose/day; ketosis can reduce this to 120 mmol/day.
- Glucose to glycogen
  - **Liver:** Lack of insulin, high glucagon signals breakdown, not synthesis.
  - **Muscle:** Lack of insulin means less transport of glucose into muscles, as well as a decreased rate of synthesis of glycogen.
- No glucose to fat in liver:
  - Low insulin, high glucagon inhibits pyruvate dehydrogenase.

CASE 4–1:
AUNT AGNES HAS DIABETES
IN POOR CONTROL

> Hyperglycemia is caused by overproduction and underutilization of glucose.

Aunt Agnes, age 70, has had non–insulin dependent diabetes mellitus for over 20 years. She has never needed insulin, but she has had to watch her diet. Last week, her doctor discovered she had high blood pressure (hypertension) and prescribed a new medication which has the side–effect of lowering levels of insulin. Agnes had a large increase in urine output, she was very thirsty and has lost several pounds of weight. Because of dizziness on standing up, she returned to the doctor, who found that the concentration of glucose in her blood was extremely high (50 mmol/l, 900 mg/dl). Explain in biochemical terms why this concentration was so high.

FIGURE 4–1
LACK OF INSULIN AND HYPERGLYCEMIA

A deficiency of insulin prevents its normal actions (indicated by the dashed lines).

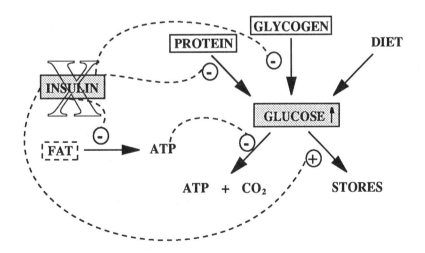

FIGURE 4–2
OXIDATION OF FATTY ACIDS PREVENTS
THE OXIDATION OF GLUCOSE

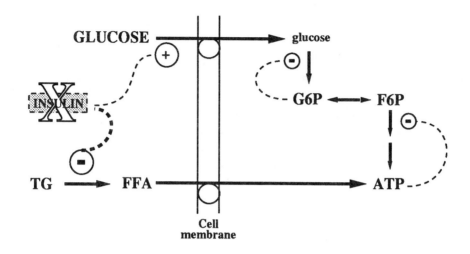

FIGURE 4–3
GLUCAGON PROMOTES THE SYNTHESIS
OF GLUCOSE IN LIVER

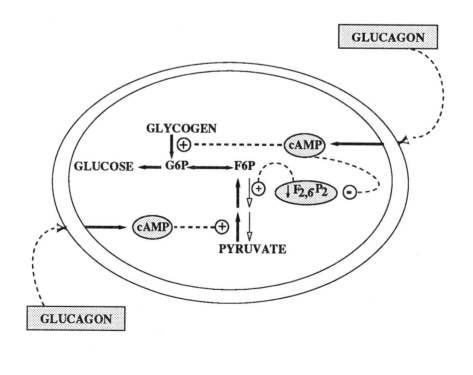

ROLE OF INSULIN
(Fig 4–2, facing page)

> Key action of insulin: inhibits the release of fatty acids from stores.

- The main stimulus for the release of insulin from ß–cells of the islets of Langerhans is a high concentration of glucose in the blood.
  - There are also other signals such as certain amino acids (leucine, arginine).
  - In addition, some hormones (e.g. alpha–adrenergics) inhibit the release of insulin, despite hyperglycemia.

> Lack of insulin signals "Between meals" despite dietary intake!

- **Insulin signals the state of energy fuel balance.** The absence of insulin causes energy metabolism to behave as if energy fuel input was too low, despite ample or excess levels in the blood. Hence, in sequence:
  - Stores of fat and protein are mobilized.
  - Fatty acids dominate as fuel for synthesis of ATP.
  - Oxidation of glucose is inhibited in all organs except the brain.
  - The concentration of glucose in the blood increases.
  - Amino acids from the breakdown of protein are converted to glucose
  - Levels of glucose increase further.
  - Ketoacids accumulate.
  - Use of glucose is now inhibited in the brain.
  - Hyperglycemia becomes more severe.
  - Glycosuria results from severe hyperglycemia.

ROLE OF GLUCAGON

> The key actions of glucagon lead to acceleration of the production of glucose in the liver.

- Glucagon accelerates the breakdown of glycogen in the liver. At the same time, it prevents the conversion of glucose to lactic and pyruvic acids (Fig 4–3).
- Glucagon promotes synthesis of the key enzymes producing glucose in the liver.

- The pool of glucose is small
- The flux through it is large

Availability of Glucose in a Normal Person

- There is very little free glucose in the body as compared to the amounts in stores or in meals (Table 4–3).
- The large flux through the small pool of free glucose has 3 main components:
  1. **Reservoir:** A large fraction of dietary glucose (perhaps half) is deposited temporarily as glycogen in the liver. This acts as a reservoir which can contain almost **10 X** the size of the pool of free glucose (Table 4–3).

     The daily flow of glucose into and out of glycogen is approximately equal to the size of the reservoir.
  2. **Supply**: Dietary carbohydrate and protein are supplied irregularly and in varied amounts. They are used mainly to fill up the store of glycogen.

     Endogenous protein is used to meet needs for glucose, when the supply of the latter in the diet is insufficient for the need of energy by the brain.
  3. **Use**: Glucose is oxidized to produce ATP. This use varies with demands for energy and can be very large or quite small. It is controlled primarily by the availability of fat fuels for ATP.

TABLE 4–3
CONTENT OF GLUCOSE IN VARIOUS COMPARTMENTS

The amount of free glucose is low relative to stores, meals or IV sources.

Compartment	Quantity of Glucose	
	(mmol)	**(g)**
As free glucose*		
– Before meals	75	13.5
– 1–2 hours after meal	150	27
Liver glycogen (fed state)	550	100
Muscle glycogen	2500	450
Amount of glucose in:		
Normal meal	500	90
1 litre D₅W	276	50

*Total in blood, in extracellular fluid and in intracellular fluid of organs not requiring insulin for the transport of glucose (liver, kidney, brain, red blood cells).

CONTROL OF THE CONCENTRATION OF GLUCOSE IN THE BLOOD

> - The pool size of glucose is very small relative to flux through it.
> - In diabetes mellitus, the major contributors to hyperglycemia are a low rate of oxidation or storage of glucose and a low rate of excretion of glucose.

- The control of the concentration of glucose in the blood is a focal point of energy metabolism, because glucose is always required for brain.
- A number of facts are important in this regard.

    1. The amount of free glucose (its pool size) is very small, 75 mmol (14 g).

    2. The daily flux through the glucose pool is very large, about 2000 mmol (360 g). The diet supplies 0–3000 mmol (0 – 540 g) of glucose per day;.

    3. The rate of synthesis of new glucose depends on the supply of precursors, dietary protein or the breakdown of body protein. Amounts are usually in the range of 200–400 mmol (36 – 72 g) glucose per day.

    4. The pathways for the use of glucose are quite limited.

        – To (and from) glycogen in liver: 550 mmol (100 g)/day.

        – To (and from) glycogen in muscle: 0–2500 mmol (0 – 450 g)/day, depending on previous depletion of this store by exercise.

        – To fat in liver: very low, usually less than 50 mmol (9 g) of glucose/day.

        – To ATP and CO_2: the only route with a potentially high rate of flux. Normally 2000 mmol (360 g)/day, but can rise up to 20–fold with vigorous exercise. Slow if fat fuels are high.

Conclusion

Control of the rate of oxidation of glucose is likely to be the major variable in the control of blood glucose (Table 4–4).

FIGURE 4–4
FAT LIMB IN DIABETES MELLITUS
IN POOR CONTROL

Fat is used to make ATP in all major organs

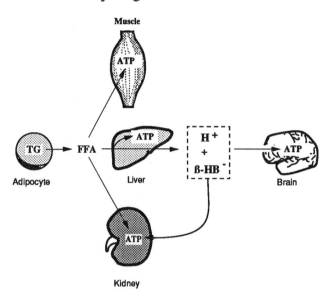

FIGURE 4–5
GLUCOSE LIMB IN DIABETES MELLITUS
IN POOR CONTROL

Glucose is produced in liver, but not used in other organs

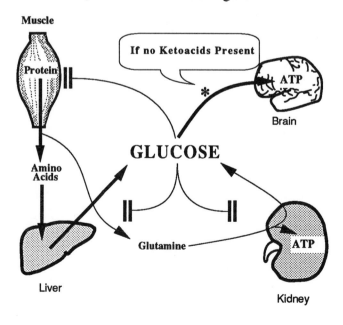

TABLE 4–4

EFFECTS OF DIABETES MELLITUS (DM) ON

OXIDATION OF GLUCOSE PER DAY

ORGAN	Glucose oxidized	Glucose to stores	Preferred fuel	Net effect of DM
BRAIN				
Normal	• 120 g	• 0	•Glucose	• Less glucose used
DM	• 30–50 g	• 0	•Ketoacids	• Decrease use due to ketosis
MUSCLE (rest)				
Normal	• 125 g	• If glycogen was depleted	• Fat and glucose	–
DM	• 0–50 g	• Low rate	• Fat	• Less glucose used due to oxidation
MUSCLE (severe exercise)				
Normal	• 1000 g +	• Glycogen store used	• Glucose to lactate and CO_2	–
DM	• 1000 g +	• Glycogen store used	• Glucose to lactate and CO_2 (if FFA not available)	• Less glucose oxidation as more FFA used
KIDNEY				
Normal	• 60 g as lactate	• 0	• Lactate	–
DM	• Produces glucose	• 0	• Ketoacids or FFA • Glutamine to glucose if acid excreted	• Less lactate oxidized and more glucose produced
LIVER				
Normal	• Produces glucose	• 100 g/day to glycogen	• ATP from amino acids	–
DM	• Produces more glucose	• Glycogen store used	• ATP from fatty acids	• More glucose produced

FIGURE 4–6
REGULATION OF THE MOVEMENT OF WATER
ACROSS CELL MEMBRANES

The circle represents the cell membrane. Water crosses this membrane very rapidly, to achieve osmotic equilibrium. Molecules such as urea also cross the membrane rapidly, and their concentration is equal in the ICF and the ECF; hence, they play no role in water distribution. The major particles, restricted largely to the ECF, are Na^+, Cl^- and HCO_3^-; the particles restricted to the ICF are predominantly organic phosphate anions together with the major ICF cation, K^+ (see Figure 4–7 for effect of glucose).

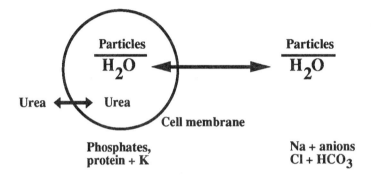

FIGURE 4–7
EFFECT OF GLUCOSE ON SHIFTS OF WATER
IN MUSCLE AND LIVER

A liver cell is shown on the right–hand side and a muscle cell on the left. The liver cell always has a [glucose] equal to that in the ECF; hence, hyperglycemia has no effect on the distribution of water between liver and the ECF. In contrast, the [glucose] in the ECF is always much higher than that in muscle cells, and thus pulls water out of muscle. This hyponatremia can cause swelling of the liver. The dotted line reflects the new ICF volumes under the influence of severe hyperglycemia.

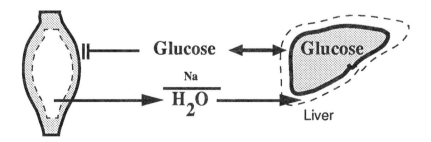

COMPLICATIONS OF HYPERGLYCEMIA

> High concentrations of glucose in blood cause problems in 3 major ways:
> – Osmotic effects
> – Acute metabolic effects
> – Non–enzymatic glycosylation of proteins

A) OSMOTIC EFFECTS

1. Osmotic Effects On Cells

(Figs 4–6 and 4–7)

- Entry of glucose into some cells (e.g. muscle) requires insulin.
  - Even with insulin, the concentration of glucose in muscle cells is very low (< 1 mmol/l) relative to that in the extracellular fluid (ECF).
- In hyperglycemia, the high concentration of glucose in the ECF provides an osmotic force, causing water to shift out of muscle and into the ECF. Organs such as liver swell because the concentration of glucose is equal to that in the ECF, whereas muscle cells shrink (Fig 4–7).
- The volume of cells in the brain does not change appreciably as 2 opposing forces of roughly equal magnitude are acting.
  - The outward force is due to the higher concentration of glucose in the ECF.
  - The inward force is hyponatremia (lower tonicity of the ECF due to a low concentration of sodium in the ECF) causing a shift of water from muscle to the brain .

2. Osmotic Effects On Urine

- Hyperglycemia causes glycosuria, because the kidney cannot reabsorb all the glucose that is filtered.
  - Glucose in urine "holds" water (and electrolytes), thereby preventing their normal reabsorption. Hence hyperglycemia causes the loss of water, sodium and potassium in the urine.
- Loss of electrolytes due to hyperglycemia can be a major threat to life in diabetics.
  - Urine in uncontrolled diabetics contains, on average, 275 mmol (50 g) of glucose/l, 50 mmol sodium/l and a variable amount of potassium.
  - Hence glycosuria causes ECF volume contraction (loss of sodium), which can lead to poor circulation and ultimately, to circulatory collapse, i.e., shock.
- Aunt Agnes's dizziness (page 53) when she stood up might have been due to loss of sodium in her urine.

EFFECTS OF SORBITOL

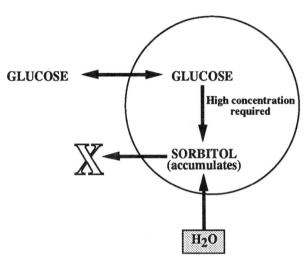

FIGURE 4–8

NON–ENZYMATIC GLYCOSYLATION

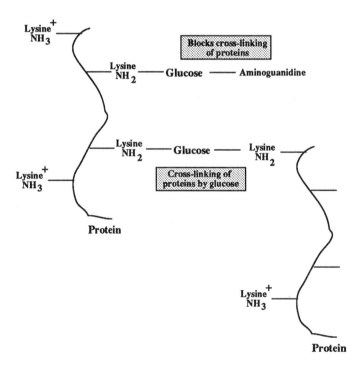

- Drugs (aminoguanidines, resemblance to lysine) are being designed to prevent binding to a second lysine by providing alternate substrates. They could retard the development of some of the complications of hyperglycemia.

B) ACUTE METABOLIC EFFECTS

Formation of Sorbitol,

(See facing page for details)

- Glucose can be reduced to sorbitol; the enzyme, aldose reductase, has a high Km for glucose and thus acts faster with hyperglycemia.

$$\text{GLUCOSE } + \text{ NADH} + \text{H}^+ \rightarrow \text{ SORBITOL } + \text{ NAD}^+$$

- Sorbitol is quite inert. It breaks down only very slowly, and accumulates in some cells, such as the lens.
  - Accumulation of sorbitol causes cells to swell. Swelling of the lens can prevent normal changes of shape, including focussing, and eventually can lead to the formation of cataracts.
- Sorbitol is converted to fructose, a better substrate for non–enzymatic glycosylation (see below).

C) NON ENZYMATIC GLYCOSYLATION

(Fig 4–8)

- Glucose and fructose can react, non–enzymatically and ultimately, irreversibly, with the exposed amino group of lysine in proteins and can also cross–link to another lysine.
- Glycosylation thus changes the charge, structure and function of these proteins. These changes may contribute to the pathology of diabetes mellitus.
- Non–enzymatic glycosylation occurs much faster with hyperglycemia than at normal levels of blood glucose.
- The product of glycosylation is removed by macrophages, cells that recognize these glycosylated proteins and destroy them. Incomplete removal of these altered proteins may contribute to some of the degenerative changes of aging.
- Glycosylated hemoglobin or albumin can be measured. Because serum albumin has a half life of 1–2 weeks, and red blood cells last for approximately 120 days, the degree of glycosylation of the two proteins indicates the degree of control over blood sugar in recent weeks and over the past 3 months, respectively.

DISCUSSION OF CASE 4–2

Why Did Jimmy Have Severe Ketoacidosis?

Two reasons for an increase in concentration of any metabolite are increased production or decreased utilisation.

1. Increased Production of Ketoacids

Ketogenesis has 2 important control sites.

(a) Extrahepatic control site for ketogenesis

- Activation of hormone–sensitive lipase (HSL) in adipose tissue (Chapter 11) is the most important stimulus for ketogenesis.

    – Low insulin, with high levels of "counter insulin" hormones in the blood, activate HSL, and thus increase the rate of delivery of FFA to the liver.

(b) Intrahepatic site

- Uptake of FFA by liver is directly proportional to their concentration in blood (see Chapter 11 for details).

- Ketogenesis in the liver increases with an increased rate of oxidation of FFA.

- There is an upper limit to ketogenesis, as ATP is a necessary by–product during ketogenesis. Quantitatively, up to 1600 mmol of ketoacids can be produced daily.

2. Decreased Utilization of Ketoacids

- Ketoacids are oxidized mainly in the brain (750 mmol/day).

- Low rates of utilization of ATP in the brain occur if the patient is in a comatose state, has taken drugs which retard cerebral metabolism or has undergone anaesthesia (see Chapter 6). Any of these might increase the degree of ketoacidosis.

**CASE 4–2:
LITTLE JIMMY DID NOT TAKE
HIS INSULIN YESTERDAY.**

Jimmy, age 11, did not take insulin yesterday because he was feeling poorly and did not eat. Ketoacidosis developed. Why?

What might cause the degree of ketoacidosis to be much worse?

- Ketoacidosis results from the overproduction of ketoacids in the liver.
- There may also be a role for underutilization of ketoacids in some circumstances.

FIGURE 4–9

LACK OF INSULIN: KETOACIDOSIS

Lack of insulin stimulates *production* of ketoacids by:

1. Deinhibiting lipolysis in adipocytes, thus;
2. Augmenting production of ketoacids in liver.

- The important site of *utilization* of ketoacids is the brain.

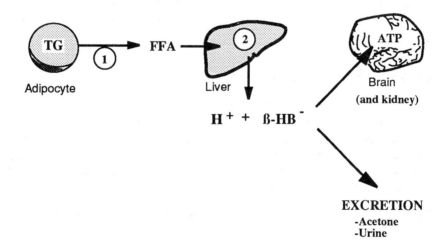

DISCUSSION OF CASE 4–3

- Since the concentrations of FFA and ketoacids in Herby's blood are still high, these are likely to be the major fuels for ATP. Hence oxidation of glucose is *not* likely to be the cause for the fall in the concentration of glucose. So what was?

1. Effects of Dilution of Glucose

- Therapy caused his ECF volume to increase from 10 to 15 l.
- Also, free glucose is present at the same concentration as in the ECF in organs such as liver and kidney, but not muscle (another 5 liters).

	Fluid accessible to glucose (liters)	
	Before therapy	After therapy
ECF	10	15
Insulin–insensitive tissues	5	5 *
	15	20

* Assume no change for simplicity; the real change is quite small.

- Thus, the original content of glucose was 50 mmol/l x 15 l or 750 mmol; if now diluted in 20 liters, the concentration of glucose would fall to 37.5 mmol/l.

2. Loss of Glucose in Urine

- ECF volume contraction caused a low urine flow; therapy increased this volume. One l of urine allowed the excretion of 250 mmol of glucose. After this excretion, the concentration of glucose should be 750 – 250 or 500 mmol/20 liters or 25 mmol/l.

3. Reduced Synthesis of Glucose?

- The rate of synthesis of glucose from protein and triglyceride glycerol is very small in comparison with the changes in the content of glucose due to dilution and urinary excretion. Given the loss of urea of 250 mmol in the urine and a decline in pool size of 180 mmol ((30 mmol/l X 40 l) – (24 mmol/l X 45 l)), the net appearance of urea is only 70 mmol. The body synthesizes close to 2 mmol of urea per mmol of glucose from protein.
- Hence only 35 mmol of glucose was added to the body in this time period via gluconeogenesis.

Conclusion

Almost the total fall in the concentration of glucose in the blood is due to dilution and excretion; insulin has had very little effect on the oxidation of glucose, due to the high concentrations of fatty acid and ketoacid anions.

CASE 4–3:
WHY DID THE CONCENTRATION
OF GLUCOSE
FALL DURING THERAPY?

Herby has a very high concentration of glucose, FFA and ketoacids in his blood and a very low extracellular fluid (ECF) volume. The correct diagnosis of diabetic ketoacidosis is made and treatment instituted. He is given insulin and 6 liters of saline, which expand his ECF volume from 10 to 15 L. He looks better; urine volume has picked up; he excreted 1 liter of urine while under observation. The levels of FFA and ketoacids in his blood are still elevated 4 hours later, but that of glucose, though still high, has fallen appreciably (see Table 4–5).

What were the main reasons for the fall in the concentration of glucose in Herby's blood?

TABLE 4–5

EFFECTS OF INSULIN PLUS SALINE
ON BLOOD AND URINE

	On diagnosis	4 hr after treatment
Fluid volume (liters)		
ECF	10	15
Urine (excreted in 4 hr)	No urine	1
Concentrations of glucose (mmol/l)		
Blood	50	24
Urine	No urine	250
Concentrations of urea (mmol/l)		
Blood	30	24
Urine	No urine	250

Hints

1. Calculate the effect of dilution on the concentration of glucose due to the extra 5 liters (net) of ECF. In addition, 5 l of intracellular fluid (ICF) contain glucose at a concentration equal to that in the ECF.

2. Calculate the quantity of glucose that was lost in the urine.

3. Calculate the amount of glucose synthesized from protein from the urea balance (urea is dissolved in the ECF and ICF; assume that ICF is 30 liters and constant in volume).

OBJECTIVES

1. To develop an approach to determine the cause for an abnormally low concentration of glucose in the blood.

2. Recognize the key metabolite which permits a separation of the major causes of hypoglycemia. This metabolite is FFA in the plasma.

3. Determine quickly if the brain has alternate fuels to provide it with ATP. In essence, this means determining whether the concentration of ketoacid anions is high or not in the blood.

REVIEW POINTS

1. Insulin and Hypoglycemia

- The most important action of insulin in promoting the oxidation of glucose is to stop the release of fat energy from its stores

- **Net Effect**: Lack of fat to burn leads to a higher rate of oxidation of glucose.

- A common misconception is that the most important metabolic effect of insulin in promoting the oxidation of glucose is to accelerate the entry of glucose into muscle cells. This is important only to promote the conversion of glucose to its store (glycogen) in muscle; this conversion will proceed only if this store of glycogen is not full.

2. Fuel Priorities and Hypoglycemia

a) Burn FFA if available in all organs except the brain. Availability depends primarily on the release of FFA from adipose tissue, in effect controlled by insulin.

b) Burn ketoacids if available and FFA are not available. This occurs in the brain during ketosis.

c) Burn glucose only if FFA and ketoacids are not available; this, in effect, means that insulin is acting.

CHAPTER 5

HYPOGLYCEMIA

APPROACH TO HYPOGLYCEMIA

- Hypoglycemia is an important condition because of the danger that the brain may not have sufficient ATP. Hypoglycemia is frequently diagnosed or suspected as a cause of symptoms.
- If the concentration of glucose in the circulation is low, look at the processes that are responsible for adding glucose to the circulation and then those that are responsible for converting it to stores or ATP. Relate these possibilities to the other important observations in the case to reach a final diagnosis.

FUNCTION/CONTROL APPROACH TO HYPOGLYCEMIA

- The key initial step is to determine if fat–derived fuels are available for oxidation. This has 2 major implications. First, if ketoacids are available, the brain will have an alternate way to synthesize its required amount of ATP. Second, if FFA are available, hyperinsulinism is not likely to be the cause of the hypoglycemia.

CASE EXAMPLES

DEFINITION OF TERMS

Hypoglycemia: Low concentration of glucose in the blood.

Hyperglycemia: High concentration of glucose in the blood.

Glucogenesis: The synthesis of glucose from pyruvate.

Gluconeogenesis: The synthesis of glucose from lactate/pyruvate where the precursor of lactate/pyruvate was not glucose (it was protein, glycerol or glycogen in muscle). This process adds new glucose to the circulation.

Glucopoenia: Too little glucose

Lipolysis: The release of FFA from its fat energy store.

Carnitine: The cofactor which is required permit the entry of FFA into mitochondria.

TABLE 5–1
EXPECTED VALUES FOR GLUCOSE IN BLOOD
DURING AND BETWEEN MEALS

Nutritional State	Glucose	
	(mmol/l)	(mg/dl)
During Meals	up to 8	up to 140
Between Meals		
• Carbohydrate phase	4.0	72
• Protein phase	3.3[a]	60
• Ketotic phase		
early	3.0[a]	54
late	4.5	81
• Terminal phase	<2.5	<45

NOTES

[a] The brain normally extracts 0.6 mmol of glucose per liter of blood flow. Hence, if there is a decline in the flow of blood or a decrease in the number of glucose transporters in the blood–brain barrier (caused by previous hyperglycemia), signs of glucopoenia (too little glucose) in the brain will occur at higher concentrations of glucose in the blood.

INTRODUCTION TO HYPOGLYCEMIA

GENERAL PRINCIPLE

• A change in concentration of a substance occurs because its rate of entry into, or removal from, the compartment has changed.

Chapter 5 is about hypoglycemia (Table 5–1). The following general points are important:

• Many clinical problems arise because normal metabolism has been disrupted, causing abnormal rates of formation and/or removal of metabolic compounds.

• Diagnosis of clinical problems depends first on clinical signs and symptoms. These suggest lines of enquiry, some of which can be assessed by measurements of the concentrations of elements or compounds in body fluids, urine or in the breath.

• To make a final diagnosis, the important clinical signs and symptoms, physical findings and laboratory data must be integrated. No abnormal finding can be ignored.

APPROACH TO A PATIENT WITH AN ABNORMAL LEVEL OF A METABOLITE IN THE BLOOD

---

1. Which is more likely; a changed rate of entry or a changed rate of removal? Be quantitative wherever posssible.
   – Use case history and biochemical knowledge.

2. Is there an important provocative feature? Look carefully at the timing of the symptoms (ie relation to meals, activity etc).
   – Use biochemical knowledge.

3. From the conclusion, predict other changes in metabolites if normal responses are present.

4. Measure the selected metabolites to determine if the responses are as expected.

5. Make your diagnosis.

TABLE 5–2
QUANTITATIVE ASPECTS OF
THE DAILY GLUCOSE BALANCE

Source of Glucose	Units (glucose per)	Quantity of Glucose (g)	(mmol)	Control
1. **Diet**				
– Carbohydrate .... day		270	1500	• Appetite or
– Protein .... day		60	333	habit
2. **Liver glycogen** .... total		100	550	• Hypoglycemia (via glucagon)
3. **Muscle glycogen** .... total		450	2500	• Exercise • Catecholamines
4. **Body protein** .... total		1500	8333	• Insulin
5. **Glycerol in** .... total fat stores		300	1650	• Lack of insulin

FOOTNOTE

1. The usual rate of breakdown of protein in the absence of trauma and infection is less than 100 g/day; thus the maximal rate of synthesis of glucose is 60 g/day.

DISCUSSION

- 1 pound = 450 g (close enough).
- If 80% water, then 90 g of protein.
- Only 60% of protein will yield glucose because some amino acids are ketogenic and because there is a 3–carbon intermediate (pyruvate). Since many amino acids have more than 3 carbons, the extras are converted to CO_2.
- Therefore, the maximum yield of glucose is 54 g (60% of 90 g).

ABNORMALITIES OF THE CONCENTRATION OF GLUCOSE IN THE BLOOD

Biochemical Aspects of Hypoglycemia

A) Entry of Glucose Into Blood
(Table 5–2)

The sources of glucose input to blood are the diet, liver glycogen, and glucogenesis.

1. Diet

- This is easy to evaluate. Hypoglycemia which is severe enough to cause symptoms will not be the result of simply an inadequate intake of glucose as the response of the body is to mobilize the alternate fuel, FFA and later, ketoacids.

2. Liver Glycogen

- A low concentration of glucose in the blood causes breakdown of glycogen in liver. The limit is the size of this store (100 g, less than 24 hour supply of glucose for the brain).
- Defects in the breakdown of glycogen may be seen in children with an inborn error of metabolism.

3. Glucogenesis

- **"New"** glucose can be made from protein, glycerol or glycogen in muscle (via lactate).
- The major site of glucogenesis is the liver; the kidneys can also make glucose.
- The possibility that hypoglycemia is due to a defect in glucogenesis can be analyzed by examining the concentration of lactate in the blood; high levels suggest a problem in glucogenesis; low levels suggest a problem in formation of lactate or its excessive oxidation.

QUESTION
(Discussion on facing page)

1. How much glucose can be synthesized from one pound of muscle ? (Assume muscle is 80 % water and 20 % protein).

FIGURE 5–1

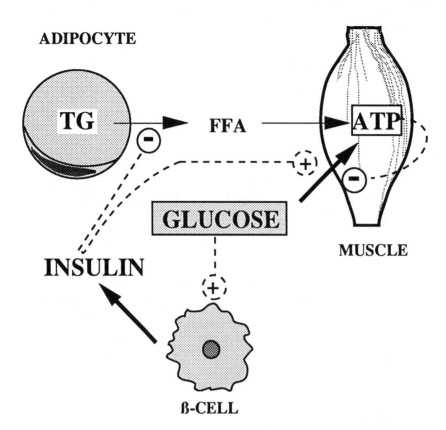

ADIPOCYTE

TG

FFA

ATP

GLUCOSE

MUSCLE

INSULIN

ß-CELL

Discussion of Questions

1. Assume that the concentration of glucose is 5 mmol/l. Glucose is distributed in the ECF and in the ICF of organs that do not require insulin for the entry of glucose (all organs except muscle and adipose tissue). In sum, this is equivalent to about half of the water in the body. In contrast, lactate is distributed in all of the body water, but its concentration in the ICF is half that in the ECF. If we assume that lactate distributes in twice the volume of glucose and that each glucose yields 2 lactates, the maximum rise in the concentration of lactate will only be 5 mmol/l..

2. With a GFR of 180 l/day, the maximal concentration of glucose which can be retained must be 1.8 g/l to filter 324 g of glucose (filtered glucose = GFR X [glucose]). In 100 ml of blood, the concentration of glucose would be 180 mg % (or 10 mmol/l). This value is called the **"renal threshold"** for glucose (the highest concentration of glucose in blood which will not allow glucose to spill into the urine).

B) Removal of Glucose From Blood

- Glucose can be used by metabolism or be lost in the urine (or rarely via other body fluids such as milk).
- Glucose is utilized by three major processes
  - Oxidation to ATP plus CO_2
  - Conversion to lactate plus ATP
  - Conversion to stores (glycogen). The synthesis of fat is very slow, so it can be ignored as a cause of hypoglycemia.

1. Conversion to ATP Plus CO_2

- The function of this pathway is to generate ATP; control is by feedback signals through ATP.
  - The most common way to increase the oxidation of glucose to CO_2 is to stop the oxidation of fat to provide ATP (Fig 5–1). The oxidation of fat is curtailed by inhibiting its release from adipose tissue or by the presence of inhibitors of fat oxidation.
  - Another cause of accelerated oxidation of glucose is a very high rate of turnover of ATP with a limited supply of fat; this may be seen in prolonged severe exercise.

2. Conversion to Lactate Plus ATP

- In the absence of oxygen, glucose is converted to lactate at a very high rate to make ATP. Accelerated glycolysis is a likely cause of hypoglycemia only during anoxia and is indicated by a high level of lactate.

3. Conversion to Stores

- The synthesis of glycogen is stimulated by insulin. Hence a low concentraion of glucose in the blood can be observed when hypoglycemia is caused by a high level of insulin.

Loss of Glucose in the Urine

- This is a rare cause of hypoglycemia.

QUESTIONS
(Discussion on the facing page)

1. How much will the concentration of lactate in the blood rise if all the glucose in the circulation were converted to lactate?

2. If the rate of filtration in the kidney (the glomerular filtration rate, GFR) is 180 liters per day in a normal adult, how high must the concentration of glucose be in the blood before glucose will appear in the urine? A normal kidney can reabsorb 325 g of glucose per day.

DISCUSSION OF QUESTIONS

3. **Time Before Symptoms**: Severe hypoglycemia occurs after the antilipolytic action of insulin has stopped the release of FFA and after the FFA and ketoacids in blood and organs have been oxidized.

    Consider the following:
    a) The brain oxidizes 5 g (close to 30 mmol) of glucose per hour.
    b) Total glucose in ECF is close to 15 g or 90 mmol.

    Therefore, the pool of glucose could feed the brain for a maximum of 3 hours if no other organ utilized glucose. However, death due to cerebral glucopoenia occurs much sooner for two reasons:
    a) Other organs oxidize glucose. If glucose were the sole fuel oxidized by all organs, the time to develop systems would fall to 45 min.
    b) The uptake of glucose by the brain declines when the concentration of glucose in blood falls. Therefore expect symptoms in 30 min or so.

4. **Effect of Glycogen in Liver**: About 100 g of glucose can be released from glycogen in liver. This could supply the brain with ATP for 20 hours if no other organ oxidizes glucose. Alternatively, glycogen in the liver could, in theory, supply the whole body with ATP for about 4 hours (the body uses 100 kcal or 25 g of glucose per hour); however, the rate of breakdown of glycogen is not fast enough to supply the minute to minute needs of the body for glucose and gluconeogenesis is a rather slow pathway (< 4 g (20 mmol/hour)); hence symptoms of hypoglycemia will occur in 60–90 minutes after insulin acts.

5. **Glycogen in Muscle to Glucose:** Since muscle lacks the terminal enzyme which converts glycogen to glucose (glucose 6–phosphatase), glycogen in muscle does not yield glucose. Thus, brain fuels are not released from muscle as glucose. However, the adrenergic response of hypoglycemia causes muscle to spare circulating glucose by 3 effects:
    a) Muscle can obtain ATP from its glycogen.
    b) Glycogen in muscle can be converted to lactate, which can provide the kidney with some or all of its needs for ATP.
    c) Circulating lactate, either provided by hepatic gluconeogenesis or via direct oxidation in the CNS, could supply some of the brain's needs for ATP.

HYPOGLYCEMIA
(Flow Chart 5–1)

> Hypoglycemia becomes a particularly important clinical problem if the delivery of other fuels (B–hydroxybutyrate or lactate) to the brain is not sufficient for its energy (ATP) needs.

- Because glucose is almost always required for the brain, hypoglycemia is the most likely way to deprive the brain of energy.
- The main clinical symptoms or signs of hypoglycemia are dysfunction of the brain and sympathetic overdrive.
  - The symptoms of rain dysfunction caused by hypoglycemia can range from some confusion to coma with or without convulsions.
  - Areas of the brain with the greatest rate of turnover of ATP or with some other underlying lesion can be the first affected. Hence, expect a wide variety of symptoms and signs as well as a range of sensitivity to a given degree of hypoglycemia.
  - Sympathetic overdrive occurs because hypoglycemia activates the sympathetic nervous system ("flight or fight response"). This causes anxiety, hyperventilation and a cold sweat (remember exam times).
  - The major cause of hypoglycemia is the lack of fat to burn. Causes are summarized in Table 5–3.

TABLE 5–3

CAUSES OF LOW LEVELS OF FFA DURING HYPOGLYCEMIA

1. Insulin
2. Insulin–like hormones (eg. insulin–like growth factors)
3. Lack of a hormone with counter–insulin actions (eg– adrenaline)
4. Drugs which may mimic the antilipolytic action of insulin (inhibit hormone sensitive lipase e.g. niacin).

QUESTIONS
(Discussion on facing page)

3. How long will it take to develop symptoms of hypoglycemia after an overdose of insulin ?
4. If the supply of glycogen in liver were converted to glucose, how long would it take before symptoms related to hypoglycemia occurred?
5. Will glycogen in muscle be converted into a brain fuel during hypoglycemia?

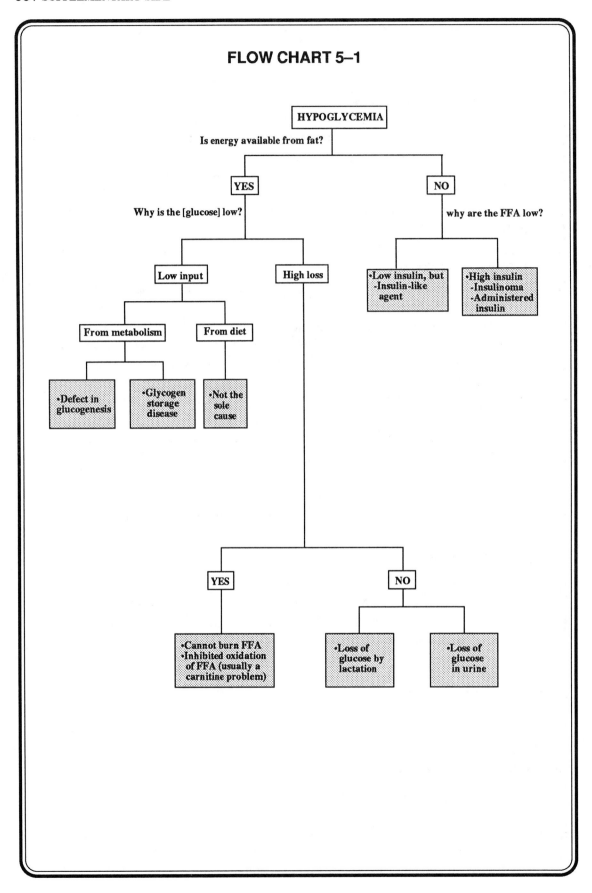

FLOW CHART 5–1

HYPOGLYCEMIA

Is energy available from fat?

YES — Why is the [glucose] low?

NO — why are the FFA low?

Low input

High loss

From metabolism

From diet

- Defect in glucogenesis
- Glycogen storage disease
- Not the sole cause

- Low insulin, but
- Insulin-like agent

- High insulin
- Insulinoma
- Administered insulin

YES

NO

- Cannot burn FFA
- Inhibited oxidation of FFA (usually a carnitine problem)

- Loss of glucose by lactation

- Loss of glucose in urine

CLINICAL APPROACH TO A PATIENT WITH HYPOGLYCEMIA

> A patient shows signs of hypoglycemia which is confirmed by direct measurement. Some blood was saved for further analysis and glucose was given to stabilize the patient. Now, what was wrong?

1. How Serious is the Hypoglycemia?

- The primary damage in hypoglycemia is to function of the brain. This danger can be especially acute if there are no alternative fuels for the brain to help reduce its dependence on glucose.

- Check the blood sample for ketoacids or lactate; if the concentration of either is above 3–5 mmol/l, hypoglycemia is not so life–threatening. Why? Ketoacids or lactic acid can provide the brain with ATP.

2. What Can Be Excluded?

- Hypoglycemia is not due solely to a low intake of glucose (unless terminal starvation); the body should have adapted to hypoglycemia with the production of ketoacids.

3. Possible Causes?

- Too little input of glucose?
- Inadequate release of glycogen from liver or a low rate of glucogenesis?
- Excessive use of glucose?
- Excess oxidation of glucose due to failure to oxidize fat (Table 5–2)?
- Low ketoacids?
- Excess use in anaerobic metabolism indicated by high lactic acid?

DISCUSSION OF CASE 5–1:
INSULIN OVERDOSE

1. Acute Insulin Overdose

- **Clinical Picture:**

  – The symptoms (CNS dysfunction, sympathetic overdrive) are consistent with this diagnosis.

- **Treatment:**

  – The acute administration of glucose as soon as a blood sample is drawn is critical. Further therapeutic decisions depend on the laboratory results, the response to glucose and why he took that dose of insulin.

- **Diagnosis:**

  – Algernon promptly recovered from all his symptoms when glucose was administered.

  – Other results of tests on the blood sample to confirm this diagnosis are:

    – Low FFA and/or ketoacid levels and an inappropriately high level of insulin in the blood.

  – Save a sample of plasma for additional tests if needed.

- **Results:**

  – The concentration of glucose in the blood was very low (1.8 mmol/l, 32 mg/dl), ketoacids were very low (< 50 μmol/l), FFA very low (<250 μmol/l), and insulin was very high.

  – These results confirm the diagnosis of insulin–induced hypoglycemia.

  – Algernon was a diabetic who took too much insulin, inadvertently. Therefore, education and vigilant follow–up were pursued.

2. The 45 Min Story

– The concentration of glucose in the blood before treatment was 100 mg/dl (5.5 mmol/l) and he has 15 liters of extracellular fluid (ECF). Thus he has 15 g of glucose in the ECF. The brain burns 5 g of glucose per hour, enough to lower the concentration of glucose by at most 1/3 in one hour. Hence we can conclude that insulin has caused other organs (e.g. muscle) to burn glucose rapidly (and almost exclusively). This reflects to a major extent, the very low availability of fat to burn due to inhibition by insulin of release from stores.

– Compare this scenario with the next case.

CASE EXAMPLES FOCUSING ON HYPOGLYCEMIA

CASE 5–1: INSULIN OVERDOSE

Algernon is suspected of taking on overdose of insulin (again); 45 min later, he is sweating, appears anxious and has a convulsion. You are at the scene.

What steps do you take for diagnosis and treatment?

What significance do you attribute to the short time between insulin dose and symptoms?

A Point to reflect on:
- Why is the brain affected during hypoglycemia? Is it simply a lack of ATP in the cells of the brain?

BACKGROUND

Turnover of ATP in Brain

- Brain makes 24000 mmol ATP/day or 16.7 mmol ATP/min.
  - Say the content of ATP in the brain is 8 mmol (for easy math). Therefore the total pool of ATP turns over every 30 sec.
  - If the fuel (glucose) level were too low for even 1 min, the brain could not function at all.

Timing

- Symptoms of hypoglycemia (sympathetic nervous system overdrive) can last 15 min before CNS function fails (convulsion).
  - Therefore there must be an early signal of lack of fuel.

Type of Early Signal

- The signal is likely to be lack of fuel and not specific for glucose as symptoms of hypoglycemia can be removed by injecting alternate fuels such as ketoacids, lactate or acetate.

Speculation

- Perhaps a cell with a high rate of turnover of ATP is the "sensor". It could have a leak for sodium requiring a high rate of NaK–ATPase, and thus be sensitive to its rate of synthesis of ATP (eg– depolarizes if there is insufficient ATP).

DISCUSSION OF CASE 5–2:
INSULINOMA

1. High Insulin, But Few Symptoms

   a) Pre–receptor events (is there enough insulin?):
   - Not the problem, as insulin levels are high.

   b) Low levels of insulin receptors:
   - Chronic high levels of insulin lead to "down–regulation" of the insulin receptor. This means that fewer receptors are now on the cell surface (more are inside cells and/or less are made).
   - Since insulin action depends on the number of hormone–receptor complexes, these will be lower for any given concentration of insulin (equation 1).

   Insulin + Receptor ↔ Insulin–receptor complex   (1)
   (ECF)   (cell membrane)

   - Notwithstanding, if the concentration of insulin rises high enough, there will be an abundance of "Insulin–receptor" complexes (equation 1). Normally, there is at least a 20–fold excess of receptors to drive equation (1) to the right and this permits a lower level of insulin in the ECF to exert its biological effects.

   - **Conclusion:** A very unlikely explanation.

   c) Post–receptor level (consider the brain as the example):
   - Brain
     - The brain does not really run out of ATP early during hypoglycemia. Long before this, it signals the rest of the body that its level of glucose is low (the sympathetic overdrive, hunger, etc) in an attempt to rectify the situation. During chronic hypoglycemia, this signal system may be less effective.
     - A second reason is that chronic hypoglycemia causes the blood–brain barrier to "up–regulate" (increase) its number of transporters of glucose. Thus more glucose can be delivered to meet the needs of the brain at a lower concentration of glucose in the blood.

(Continued on supplementary side page 69)

CASE 5–2:
INSULINOMA

Bertha has a tumor of the ß–cells of her pancreas that produces insulin on an intermittent, but chronic basis. She has a surge of insulin release which is even higher than that of Algernon in Case 5–1, but has few symptoms. Why?

1. Discuss the problem from a point of view that considers insulin and its binding to its receptor on the cell membrane.

Receptors

Hormones act on cells by binding to specific receptors which tell the cell that the hormone is exerting a signal.

Insulin + Receptor $\leftrightarrow$ **Insulin–Receptor complex**
(cell surface)   (leads to cell response)

This case is continued on page 69.

DISCUSSION OF CASE 5–2:
INSULINOMA
(continued)

2. Muscle and Fuel Consumption:

- Muscle can burn 5 g of glucose per min during vigorous exercise. Hence, if it only burns glucose, muscle can consume 2/3 of the pool of glucose in 2 minutes.

- Three hypotheses can explain why Bertha can exercise for 3 minutes without symptoms:

  a) She burns endogenous fuels (glycogen) in muscle.

  b) Muscle has an exogenous fuel (FFA).

  c) Acceleration of transport of glucose by insulin is not a critically important action of insulin in this setting.

- All three hypotheses are correct.

  a) Glycogen is burnt.

  b) *Levels of FFA are not low despite actions of insulin.* This probably reflects the chronically high levels of adrenergic hormone which stimulate lipolysis in adipose tissue to a greater degree than in the situation where there was an acute infusion of insulin. Also the low level of glucose in the circulation does not permit enough uptake of glucose into adipocytes to re–esterify the FFA, so net formation of FFA is quite high (however, there is no increase in ketoacids as the liver still responds to insulin).

  c) Burning FFA in muscle leads to the formation of acetyl–CoA, NADH, and ATP, which inhibit pyruvate dehydrogenase and glycolysis in muscle. Glycolysis is inhibited non–competitively at the reaction catalyzed by hexokinase (this means that glucose cannot be used in glycolysis no matter how much its concentration in intracellular fluid rises). Therefore antilipolysis may be more important than accelerated transport of glucose in the case of an insulinoma.

Note:

The above interpretations may be a little too enthusiastic. We provided a rationale to explain why less (not no) glucose is used in muscle. Patients with an insulinoma will become symptomatic when they exercise, but this occurs later than expected (if glucose was the only important energy fuel at this time).

CASE 5–2:
INSULINOMA
(continued)

2. Bertha can run to catch a train (3 minutes of vigorous exercise) without becoming symptomatic. What does this mean in biochemical terms (fuels being oxidized in muscle)? Another way to look at this is, which action of insulin in muscle is more important in causing hypoglycemia, accelerated transport of glucose or provision of energy as FFA?

   Fig 5–2 may help with this case. Insulin controls the release of FFA and also the synthesis of ketoacids.

FIGURE 5 – 2

INSULIN AND THE CONTROL OF
THE UTILIZATION OF GLUCOSE

   The oxidation of FFA or ketoacids generates acetyl–CoA, NADH and ATP and thus inhibits pyruvate dehydrogenase in consumer tissues. This prevents the use of pyruvate as a precursor of ATP. ATP (and citrate) inhibit glycolysis and ultimately prevent the oxidation of glucose, no matter how high its concentration in the cell (see Chapter 8 for details).

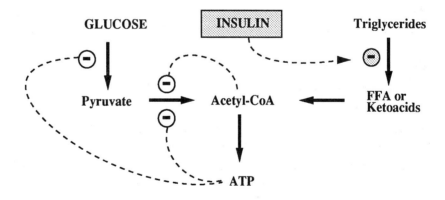

DISCUSSION OF CASE 5–3:
FASTING HYPOGLYCEMIA
WITH FFA BUT WITHOUT KETOACIDS

1. **Hyperglycemia with or without ketosis:** The serious and acute picture suggests that other brain fuels are absent – i.e., without ketoacids.

2. **Biochemical site:** Since the level of FFA in plasma is high, there is no inhibition of hormone–sensitive lipase (HSL) in adipose tissue. Hence this is not a problem of high levels of insulin.

    The low ketoacids indicate a failure to oxidize FFA to ketoacids in the liver. There are many potential lesions (see Fig 5–3). Since Reggie is not an infant and it is his first episode, an inborn error of metabolism is unlikely. Suspect a toxin inhibiting the oxidation of FFA in the liver.

3. **Why so long after meals?** Since his brain was deprived of ATP by 6 hours, either he cannot mobilize glycogen from his liver or he is burning glucose for all his caloric needs because oxidation of FFA is inhibited and all the ATP now comes from glucose.

4. **Levels of FFA:** The findings suggest that FFA are available, but there is a failure to oxidize FFA in the liver. From Fig 5–4, a very likely lesion is the absence of carnitine (needed to transport fatty acyl–CoA into mitochondria). Other possibilities include an inhibition of the uptake of FFA into cells, or of their conversion to CoA esters, or a defect in the synthesis of ketoacids.

    Fuels for other organs: Fat cannot be oxidized and there are no ketoacids, so all tissues are burning glucose (or amino acids).

5. **Treatment:** Avoid further intake of the toxin, give exogenous carnitine and provide glucose constantly to avoid damage of the brain due to hypoglycemia.

    Quantitative Aspects:
    - If Reggie expends 100 kcal/hr, then 25 g/hr of glucose are needed; lower rates of glucose infusion are needed if Reggie is not active and expends less kcal/hr.
    - Since the degree of activity cannot be controlled with precision, the rate of infusion of glucose must be monitored closely.
    - Recall that size of the pool or glucose is really very small (close to 15 g in an adult) and that severe hyperglycemia must also be avoided.

    Final Diagnosis:
    - Reggie ate an unripe Ackee–Ackee fruit, which contains a toxin that inactivates carnitine.

CASE 5–3:
FASTING HYPOGLYCEMIA WITH
HIGH FFA BUT
WITHOUT KETOACIDS

Reggie, a 27 year old in Jamaica, was brought to the emergency room while having a convulsion. His skin was cold and clammy. You suspect that he is suffering from hypoglycemia. What should be done?

QUESTIONS
(Discussion on facing page)

1. If Reggie suffers from hypoglycemia, is it likely to be the type which is associated with ketosis?

2. Analysis of a sample of his blood was performed in the emergency room. The concentration of glucose in the blood was indeed low (2.0 mmol/l or 36 mg/dl). In the same sample of blood, the levels of FFA were high, but the concentration of ketoacids was very low. Identify the biochemical site of the lesion (Fig 5–3).

FIGURE 5–3

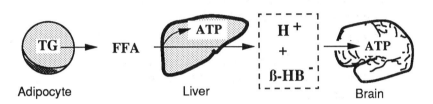

3. Reggie was well during and shortly after meals, but became hypoglycemic five to six hours after the last meal. Why?

4. Why are the levels of FFA in his plasma high and the concentration of ketoacids low when he is symptomatic? How does this help in your differential diagnosis?

5. What treatment will you recommend?

FIGURE 5–4

CAUSES FOR LOW OXIDATION OF FFA

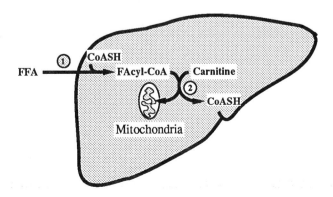

DISCUSSION OF CASE 5–4:
HYPOGLYCEMIA
3 HOURS AFTER MEALS

1. **Why 3 hours after a meal?** Each meal contains some 90 g of carbohydrate and the stomach empties its contents into the small intestine in about 3 hours. Thus, in the three hour period of relative physical inactivity, the body has to process 90 g or 360 kcal of glucose. Given a normal rate of caloric expenditure of some 100 kcal/hr, the body is provided with more glucose than it needs for total body ATP needs (let alone the other fuels of the diet). Accordingly, this patient has the signal for storage of glucose (elevated levels of insulin).

2. **Counter–insulin hormones:** The insulin signals for storage of glucose is balanced by the *counter insulin hormones*, glucagon, glucocorticoids, adrenaline and thyroid hormone. This patient's symptoms are consistent with destruction of the adrenals; hence lack of glucocorticoids is likely.

3. **Glucocorticoids and hypoglycemia:** Hypoglycemia is the result of a low rate of production of glucose in the liver consequent to the lack of glucocorticoid. The two pathways to consider are glycogenolysis and glucogenesis; both are reduced when levels of glucocorticoid are abnormally low:

    a) **Glycogenolysis:** Lack of glucocorticoids impairs the signal for the breakdown of glycogen (see Chapter 8 for details).

    b) **Glucogenesis:** The 2 sites of action are extrahepatic and intrahepatic.

      – Extrahepatic. The mobilization of the precursors for glucogenesis (net protein catabolism) is accelerated by glucocorticoids (and diminished in their absence).

      – Intrahepatic. Glucocorticoids are responsible for intrahepatic events such as the induction of key enzymes promoting glucogenesis.

4. **Treatment.** Treatment should consist of administration of glucose to deal with the acute problem and then glucocorticoid (and mineralocorticoid) replacement therapy to deal with the problem with her adrenal gland.

CASE 5–4:
HYPOGLYCEMIA 3 HOURS
AFTER MEALS

Sophie had disseminated tuberculosis one year ago. Even though antibiotic therapy cured the tuberculosis, she never recovered her strength and noted that her skin had developed dark pigmentation (this sign reflects a problem with her adrenal gland).

She has symptoms and signs of hypoglycemia 3 hours after eating a meal; these symptoms disappeared with feeding of sweetened orange juice. The level of FFA in the plasma was not elevated. This suggests that the cause of hypoglycemia is hyperinsulinism.

A list of potential causes is provided in Table 5–4.

TABLE 5–4

CAUSES OF HYPERINSULINISM IN HYPOGLYCEMIA

1. Absolute Elevation of Insulin.
   - Presence of other insulin secretagogues
   - Certain amino acids
   - Drugs such as chlorpropamide
   - Decreased levels of inhibitors of insulin release from ß–cells
   - Abnormal ß–Cells
   - Insulinoma

2. Relative Elevation of Insulin or Prolonged Insulin Action:
   - Low levels of counter–insulin hormones.
   - Drugs with an antilipolytic action.

QUESTIONS
Discussion on facing page)

1. What is the significance of hypoglycemia which occurs 3 hours after a meal?
2. What are the usual "counter–insulin" hormones?
3. How does the lack of a hormone such as glucocorticoid lead to the development of hypoglycemia?
4. What are your recommendations for treatment?

DISCUSSION OF CASE 5–5:
HYPOGLYCEMIA
WHICH OCCURS BETWEEN MEALS

1. **Expected level of metabolites:** The problem in this patient is a low rate of hepatic glucogenesis. Hence, expect hypoglycemia and an elevated concentration of precursors of glucose (lactate, alanine). Although hepatic glucogenesis is needed to process a high dietary protein load, its other use is to provide circulating glucose when this metabolite is not supplied by the diet. As a consequence of hypoglycemia, insulin levels fall and the levels of FFA and ketoacids in the blood should be high between meals.

2. **Development of hypoglycemia:** Since her problem is with production of glucose, hypoglycemia will be found between meals, not during meals.

3. **Level of ketoacids in plasma:** During sustained hypoglycemia, there is reduced release of insulin (reflecting the lack of glucose–stimulated release of insulin) leading to high levels of FFA and augmented hepatic ketogenesis. Hence the concentration of ketoacids in the blood should be high between meals.

4. **Cerebral signs of hypoglycemia:** Early in hypoglycemia, CNS signs may be evident. With time, as levels of ketoacids in plasma rise, these signs of hypoglycemia should diminish. However, as glycogen in the liver has gone, she will not survive without dietary glucose.

5. **Concentration of lactate in plasma in fasting:** The concentration of lactate tends to fall to low levels as fasting progresses in normals. In contrast, patients with a defect in hepatic glucogenesis should have a much higher concentration of lactate in the blood, reflecting low rates of glucogenesis in the liver and of lactate oxidation in all tissues caused by inhibition of PDH by the high rates of oxidation of FFA and ketoacids (Fig 5–2).

6. **Contrast in symptoms in a patient with glucose 6–phosphatase (G6Pase) deficiency:** Hypoglycemia in patients with a defect in the middle of the pathway of glucogenesis occurs more slowly than in patients with a defect in the final step (G6Pase) because G6Pase is also needed for release of glucose from glycogen. Patients who cannot convert hepatic glycogen to glucose (G6Pase deficiency) would be expected to have symptoms related to hypoglycemia as soon as dietary glucose is not present. They also should have a large liver, "stuffed" with glycogen, and develop lactic acidosis more readily during fasting owing to hepatic glycogenolysis and to very high levels of G6P (and F6P) in the liver.

CASE 5–5:
HYPOGLYCEMIA WHICH OCCURS
BETWEEN MEALS

Alice, aged 2, has an enzyme defect in glucogenesis in the liver (low activity of the enzyme fructose 1,6 bisphosphatase, see site 2 in Fig 5–5).

QUESTIONS
(Discussion on facing page)

1. What pattern of metabolites would you expect to find in her blood?
2. Will she develop hypoglycemia in the fed or fasted state?
3. Should there be an elevated concentration of ß–hydroxybutyrate in her plasma?
4. Will she have cerebral signs related to hypoglycemia?
5. What will the concentration of blood lactate in her blood be between meals?
6. In what way would the signs and syptoms differ if Alice had a deficiency of the release of glucose from glycogen in the liver?

FIGURE 5–5

KEY STEPS IN HEPATIC PRODUCTION
OF GLUCOSE

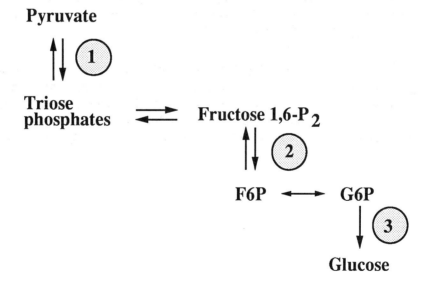

DISCUSSION OF CASE 5–6:
ETHANOL–INDUCED HYPOGLYCEMIA

1. **Brain symptoms:** Since patients with hypoglycemia caused by the metabolism of ethanol have ketoacidosis, the brain has an alternative precursor for ATP from the outset, and it should not suffer so acutely from lack of glucose. Note that CNS symptoms can occur because of a lack of vitamin B_1 in chronic alcoholics, or because of high levels of ethanol.

2. **Timing:** Hypoglycemia will only develop after the store of glycogen in the liver has been depleted. Thus it will be a late symptom, often after several days of fasting.

3. **Infusion of glucose:** These subjects are usually deficient in insulin as a result of the alpha–adrenergic response to a low ECF volume (secondary to vomiting) and/or alcohol withdrawal; they are therefore ketonemic. Hence, their activity of PDH is reduced until the elevated level of ketoacids has disappeared. Thus, administered glucose will be retained in the blood and cause hyperglycemia. One liter of 5% dextrose in water has 50 g of glucose (3 X the body pool size for glucose). Since the volume of distribution of glucose is close to 16 L owing to the contracted ECF volume, the concentration of glucose in the blood will rise by as much as 300 mg/dl or 15–20 mmol/l; glycosuria will develop and may lead to additional fluid and electrolye problems.

4. **Dangers of an infusion of glucose:** Patients who vomit have a very low content of potassium. Deficiency of insulin masks the extracellular deficit of potassium by causing a shift of potassium out of cells. Administration of glucose may raise the concentration of insulin in the blood which causes potassium to enter cells and thus to hypokalemia. A deficit of potassium in the extracellular can lead to abnormal heart rhythms (and possibly death).

   - **Deficiency of thiamine.** A patient with a deficiency of vitamin B_1 (thiamine) has a defect in the oxidation of pyruvate, Thus the brain can only metabolize glucose to lactic acid for the synthesis of ATP; this rate is extremely fast and yields a huge hydrogen ion load which can destroy areas of the brain which have rapid rates of turnover of ATP (called the Wernicke–Korsakoff Syndrome).

CASE 5–6:
ETHANOL–INDUCED HYPOGLYCEMIA

Ed develops hypoglycemia following the ingestion of ethanol.

QUESTIONS
(Discussion on facing page)

1. Will this hypoglycemia be associated with brain symptoms?
2. How long will it take to develop severe hypoglycemia?
3. What will happen to the concentration of glucose in his blood if 1 liter of D_5W (5% dextrose and water) is given over 30 min?
4. What are the dangers of administering glucose?

BACKGROUND

• Metabolism of ethanol can cause hypoglycemia by lowering the rate of hepatic glucogenesis. Two mechanisms can be envisioned:
  – The high levels of NADH in hepatocytes should lower the concentrations of pyruvate and oxaloacetate which are metabolized by NAD–linked dehydrogenases.
  – Metabolism of ethanol yields ATP in the liver; so does the pathway of amino acids to glucose. The ability of the liver to use ATP is limited, and can restrict conversion of amino acids to glucose, especially if metabolism of ethanol is also leading to the synthesis of ATP.

FIGURE 5–6

EFFECT OF ETHANOL ON HEPATIC GLUCOSE PRODUCTION

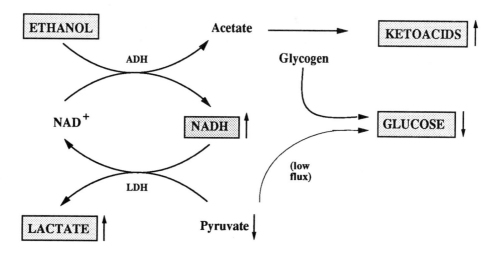

ADH = alcohol dehydrogenase
LDH = lactate dehydrogenase

DISCUSSION OF CASE 5–7:
TUMOR–INDUCED HYPOGLYCEMIA

The question poses 3 hypotheses for the hypoglycemia:

1. Hypoglycemia Due to Insulin Action
(see Discussion of Case 5–1 and 5–2)

- If so, the circulating FFA and ketoacids would be low, because the insulin or insulin–like agent causes antilipolysis in adipocytes and decreases the rate of ketogenesis in the liver.

2. Hypoglycemia Due to Excessive Consumption of Glucose

- If so, the concentration of insulin in the plasma will be low and FFA plus ketoacids will be high. Tumors often have a high production of lactate with or without hypoxia; the reason for this is not completely clear.

- Symptoms of hypoglycemia will occur between meals. A large quantity of glucose may be needed to avoid hypoglycemia. Theoretically, as much as 500 g of glucose could be required in a subject expending 2000 kcal.

- If there is excessive conversion of glucose to lactate by the tumor, there will be hypoglycemia together with a high concentration of lactate and a low concentration of bicarbonate in the blood.

3. Inhibition of Hepatic Gluconeogenesis
(see Discussion of Case 5–4)

- If so, insulin will be low and FFA plus ketoacids will be high in the plasma; the levels of lactate and alanine in the plasma should also be high.

- Symptoms will develop only after depletion of hepatic glycogen or later in the fasted period. Symptoms should respond to a lower rate of infusion of glucose than in hypothesis 2.

CASE 5–7:
TUMOR–INDUCED HYPOGLYCEMIA

Grace, who has a very large tumor burden, develops hypoglycemia. The tumor is a large sarcoma (a connective tissue malignancy which can grow rapidly to an immense size, so that it usually has a large necrotic center; it can also secrete peptides which act like insulin).

The mechanisms by which hypoglycemia can develop in Grace are shown in Fig 5–7.

FIGURE 5–7

TUMOR–INDUCED HYPOGLYCEMIA

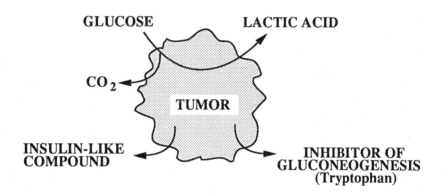

QUESTION
(Discussion on facing page)

Several mechanisms are suggested for the hypoglycemia (Fig 5–7).

a) Release of insulin or an insulin–like agent by the tumor.

b) Consumption of glucose by the tumor.

c) Inhibition of glucogenesis in the liver by one of the products of the necrotic tumors.

How would you know which mechanism is operating?

BACKGROUND

Carnitine corrects the problem, so Bonnie probably has hypoglycemia due to a lack of carnitine (Fig 5–4). Problems exist in organs which require oxidation of FFA. Involvement of the brain is a secondary event due to hypoglycemia with the absence of ketoacids. Furthermore, organs provided with more FFA (lack of insulin secondary to hypoglycemia) than they can oxidize (lack of carnitine) convert FFA to triglycerides, further compromising their function.

DISCUSSION OF CASE 5–8:
HYPOGLYCEMIA IN THE NEWBORN

1. **Hypoglycemia.** This results from a high rate of oxidation of glucose in those organs that cannot oxidize FFA. Symptoms occur when FFA should be oxidized to provide ATP i.e., between meals.

2. **Hyperammonemia.** Hyperammonemia reflects low rates of synthesis of urea consequent to low rates of generation of ATP in the liver between meals (glucose is utilized at a slow rate by the liver and hypoglycemia is present). Second, there is increased net breakdown of protein owing to hypoglycemia.

3. **Lack of ketonemia**: A low rate of oxidation of FFA in the liver is secondary to the deficit of carnitine (Fig 5–4).

4. **Lipid deposition**: Low levels of insulin secondary to hypoglycemia cause a high delivery of FFA from adipocytes. The rate of oxidation of FFA is low, owing to the lack of carnitine. Hence esterification of these FFA could occur and lead to accumulation of triglycerides.

5. **Familial problem.** The fact that a similar lesion was found in a sibling suggests a hereditary basis for this disorder. In this case, the problem may be in the uptake of carnitine from the circulation.

6 **Other tissues.** Lack of carnitine prevents oxidation of FFA to yield ATP in both of these types of muscle (cardiac and skeketal). Since FFA cannot be converted to ketoacids in the liver, there is no synthesis of this potential fuel for the brain between meals, though the brain does not suffer **directly** from the inability to oxidize FFA.

CASE 5–8:
HYPOGLYCEMIA IN THE NEWBORN

Bonnie, who is 7 months old, was admitted for investigation of hypoglycemia. She had multiple previous admissions for cardiac failure, central nervous system disorder, and/or hepatomegaly (large liver).

- On each admission, hypoglycemia was present (1 mmol/l, 18 mg/dl).

- One brother had died at age 3 months with similar findings.

- Physical examination revealed weakness and reduced muscle tone.

- Laboratory findings revealed hypoglycemia, high levels of FFA, negative test for serum ketoacids, hyperammonemia (150 umol/l, normal less than 35 umol/l), plasma carnitine level was normal but there was a mild elevation of enzymes released from liver and muscle.

- Dietary studies revealed that ketoacids were not produced in response to fasting, and hypoglycemia developed after 10 hours of fasting.

- Tissue biopsies revealed fat accumulation in muscle and liver. Levels of carnitine in liver and muscle were markedly reduced.

- When given supplements of carnitine, the symptoms and signs disappeared.

  In what organ is the basic defect?

QUESTIONS
(Discussion on facing page)

1. What was the cause of hypoglycemia in Bonnie?
2. Why is the concentration of ammonium high?
3. Why is the concentration of ketoacids low?
4. Why are there lipid deposits in the liver?
5. What is the significance of the fact that similar findings were seen in Bonnie's brother?
6. What importance do you attribute to the fact that Bonnie also had involvement of cardiac muscle, skeletal muscle and the CNS?

TABLE 6–1

POSSIBLE CAUSES OF LACTIC ACIDOSIS

- Lack of oxygen
  - Lung problem
  - Circulatory problem
  - Hemoglobin problem
- Compromised metabolism of lactate without hypoxia
  - Formation of lactic acid is too high (high glycolysis owing to low ATP)
    - Exercise, uncoupler of oxidative phosphorylation
  - Breakdown of lactic acid is too low
    - PDH problem (Vitamin B_1 deficit, inborn error)
    - Liver problem
      - destruction or replacement of the liver
      - defect in glucogenesis
        - inborn error
        - inhibitor of glucogenesis (eg, drugs, ethanol, tryptophan)

TABLE 6–2

POSSIBLE CAUSES OF KETOACIDOSIS

- Normal pancreas
  - Hypoglycemia
    - fasting
    - defect in glucogenesis
    - glycogen storage disease
  - Suppression of insulin release
    - drugs (eg, diuretics, dilantin)
    - adrenaline (low ECF volume), commonly seen in ethanol abuse

- Destroyed pancreatic cells
  - Diabetes mellitus
  - Chronic pancreatitis
  - Rare diseases e.g. hemochromatosis

CHAPTER 6

METABOLIC ACIDOSIS

LACTIC ACIDOSIS

• The accumulation of lactic acid is very important from a medical perspective as the physician must make quick decisions with respect to therapy and the conditions that underlie the accumulation of lactic acid are quite common.

• The most common cause of lactic acidosis is hypoxia, during which acid (protons) can accumulate so rapidly that they might kill the patient in minutes. Thus the only viable therapy in this situation is to increase the delivery of oxygen to organs.

Case 6–1   Lactic Acidosis With Hypoxia.

Case 6–2   Lactic Acidosis Without Hypoxia.

Case 6–3   Lactic Acidosis in an Alcoholic.

KETOACIDOSIS

• Ketoacids can accumulate in patients with a low level of insulin.

• The rate of production of ketoacids is not nearly as rapid as the rate of production of lactic acid.

• The rate of removal of the ketoacids mainly reflects the rate of energy metabolism in the brain.

Case 6–4   Ketoacidosis With Hyperglycemia.

Case 6–5   Ketoacidosis in an Alcoholic.

Case 6–6   Ketoacidosis in acute Alcohol Intoxication

ANION GAP

> • A calculation of diagnostic convenience to detect unusually high concentrations of organic acids in the blood.

• The number of positively charged ions must equal the number of negatively charged ions in the plasma.

• Measured cations (Na^+) + unmeasured cations ($K^+ + Mg^{++} + Ca^{++}$) = Measured anions ($Cl^- + HCO_3^-$) + unmeasured anions (albumen + organic anions).

   – Unmeasured cations do not vary much in concentration

   – Unmeasured anions like albumen can be assessed readily (measured).

   – Therefore a rise in the anion gap of plasma is determined mainly by a rise in the concentration of organic anions.

• Usual organic acids are lactic acid and ketoacids.

• Quantities in plasma are:

   – $Na - (Cl + HCO_3)$ = 12 ± 2 meq/l

   – Albumen accounts for almost all of the usual anion gap

   – The concentrations of K^+, Mg^{++} and Ca^{++} do not change appreciably

   – The rise in the anion gap above its normal value of 12 meq/l is usually equal to the fall in the concentration of bicarbonate. Thus typical values are:

		Normal	**Lactic Acidosis**
Na .... mmol/l		140	140
Cl .... mmol/l		103	103
HCO$_3$ .... mmol/l		25	25-15 = 10
Anion gap .... meq/l		12	12 + 15 = 27

ACCUMULATION OF H⁺
IN THE BLOOD

- High concentrations of H^+ may:
  - depress the function of the heart
  - alter the activity of key enzymes and transporters
- Hence accumulation of H^+ must be avoided, if possible.

Two types of metabolic acidosis relate directly to energy metabolism:

1. **Lactic acidosis:**
   - For the most part, this extra lactic acid accumulates when the demand for oxygen exceeds its delivery to tissues (Table 6–1).

2. **Ketoacidosis:**
   - Ketoacids are produced in large quantities when there is a relative lack of insulin (Table 6–2).

HOW MANY H⁺ ARE
TOO MANY?

- The normal concentration of H^+ in blood is 40 nmol/l (pH 7.4);
  - an increase to 64 nmol/l (pH 7.2) is serious, and an increase to 100 nmol/l (pH 7.0) is life–threatening. Yet the addition of metabolic acids (lactic acid or ketoacids) can easily be 5,000,000 nmol/l in the blood.
- As H^+ accumulate, some can be bound, temporarily, by buffers in the body. This buffering only occurs when there is an elevated concentration of H^+.
- The major buffers are:
  - *Intracellular proteins*: Close to 2/3 of this buffering occurs inside cells, predominantly on cell proteins. By binding H^+, these proteins become more positively charged, and this may change their function.
  - *Bicarbonate buffer system* inside and outside cells.

QUANTITIES

- For each 0.1 unit change in pH, buffers of the body can bind close to 200 mmol of H^+.
- To *eliminate* H^+ (buffers only minimize the rise in concentration of H^+), H^+ must be metabolized along with an anion or they must be excreted in the urine (See Chapter 2).

QUANTITATIVE ANALYSIS
OF RATE OF
FORMATION OF LACTIC ACID

- The rate of consumption of oxygen at rest is close to 12 mmol/min
  - Each atom of oxygen will support the synthesis of approximately 3 molecules of ATP (P:O ratio of 3); hence 72 mmol ATP will be formed per min. If 72 mmol of ATP were derived from anaerobic glycolysis, the rate of synthesis of lactic acid would have to be 72 mmol/min (6ATP/O_2 and 1 ATP/lactic acid).

$$\text{Glucose} \rightarrow 2\,\text{ATP} + 2\,\text{H}^+ + 2\,\text{Lactate}$$

- Glycolysis begins with glucose or glycogen.
  - The total content of free glucose in the body is close to 100 mmol (5 mmol/l X close to 20 l, the volume in which glucose is present).
  - Since each molecule of glucose can be converted into 2 molecules of lactic acid, only 200 mmol of lactic acid and ATP can be produced from free glucose (about 3 min worth of ATP!).

- The liver contains close to 600 mmol of glucose as glycogen (100 g but each glucose residue weighs 162 g in glycogen)
  - This will yield 1200 mmol of lactic acid (about 18 min worth of ATP!).

- Owing to its large mass, muscle contains 3–4–fold more glycogen than liver.
  - Hence muscle could produce about 4000 mmol of lactic acid if there were a stimulus for the breakdown of its glycogen (exercise, catecholamines).

• Summary

  - Not only is there an acid–base threat in anoxia, there is a threat of a "lack of ATP" as well, because of a relatively low supply of glucose.
  - Organs at greatest risk are those with a rapid rate of turnover of ATP and a low content of potential buffers for H^+, mainly the brain.

ACCUMULATION OF LACTIC ACID

> • A rise in the concentration of lactic acid results from increased input, decreased consumption or both.

• Lactic acid accumulates when the supply of oxygen is not adequate.

$$\text{Glucose} + 2\,\text{ADP} + 2\,\text{Pi} \rightarrow 2\,\text{ATP} + 2\,\text{Lactate}^- + 2\,\text{H}^+ \qquad (1)$$

– Flux through anaerobic glycolysis is very rapid. It has the potential to meet the needs for ATP in most tissues for short periods of time. The acid load from anaerobic glycolysis can be life–threatening in minutes.

• Lactic acid can also be produced during the oxidation of amino acids.

$$\text{Alanine} \rightarrow \text{Lactate}^- + \text{NH}_4^+ \qquad (2)$$
$$2\,\text{NH}_4^+ + 2\,\text{HCO}_3^- \rightarrow \text{Urea} \qquad (3)$$

– This is a very slow pathway; the potential threat to the body is from the load of NH_4^+ (equation 2) which is removed as urea (equation 3).

FIGURE 6–1

SOURCES OF INPUT OF LACTIC ACID

Glycolysis is the major *source* of lactate.

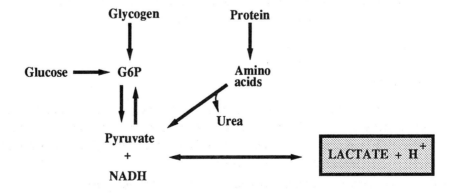

QUANTITATIVE ANALYSIS OF BREAKDOWN OF LACTIC ACID

Oxidation to ATP Plus CO_2

- The rates of formation and removal of lactic acid can be compared by examining the balance for ATP
  - In anaerobic glycolysis, each mol ATP is formed with 1 mol of H^+.
  - When oxygen returns, each mol of lactic acid oxidized will form 18 mol of ATP.
  - Hence, removal of lactate requires 18 times the turnover of ATP than does its formation.
- During anoxia, the rate of production of lactic acid is 72 mmol/min if balance of ATP is achieved. If no other fuel is oxidized when oxygen returns, the maximal rate of oxidation of lactic acid is 4 mmol/min (72 ATP per min/18 ATP per lactic acid). This is obviously an overestimate as the brain will probably burn glucose and there will likely be some oxidation of fatty acids elsewhere in the body.

Glucogenesis

- Conversion of 1 mol of lactate to 0.5 mol of glucose consumes 3 mol of ATP
  - equivalent to 0.5 mol of O_2 (P/O ratio is 3).
- Blood flow to the liver is close to 1 l/min (each l has only 6 mmol of oxygen)
  - $2/3$ of hepatic blood flow is delivered first to the GI tract which extracts 20 % of the oxygen).
- The maximal possible rate of glucogenesis in the liver is 12 mmol per min.
  - This is an overestimate because the usual rate of extraction of oxygen by the liver is approximately 2 mmol/min; accordingly, a reasonable estimate for the maximal rate of conversion of lactate to glucose is 3–4 mmol/min.
  - When a similar analysis is done for the kidneys, the maximum rate of production of glucose from lactate is close to 0.5 mmol/min.

SUMMARY

- If lactate is the sole fuel oxidized, at rest, in all organs except the brain, and glucogenesis is proceeding at its most rapid rate, the maximal rate of disposal of lactate is 6–7 mmol/min. This maximum is never achieved, and a more reasonable estimate would be less than half this rate.
- Compare these estimates to those for the input of lactate, page 78.

CONSUMPTION OF LACTIC ACID
(Fig 6–2 and facing page)

There are two major and two minor routes for *removal* of lactate.

- The major routes are:
    1. Oxidation of lactate to ATP plus CO_2 in any organ with mitochondria and a supply of oxygen; this involves reconversion of lactate to pyruvate and must go through PDH.
    2. Lactate (plus a H^+) can be converted to glucose mainly in the liver , but also in the kidney.

- The minor pathways have a very slow rate of flux and hence will not be considered further. They are:
    1. Conversion to storage triglyceride.
    2. Conversion to certain amino acids in the liver.

FIGURE 6–2

CONSUMPTION OF LACTATE

The major pathways for the removal of lactate are oxidation to provide ATP and conversion to glucose. The former requires flux through PDH and is regulated by negative feedback by ATP. If this pathway is inhibited, the only major fate for lactate is conversion to glucose, primarily in the liver.

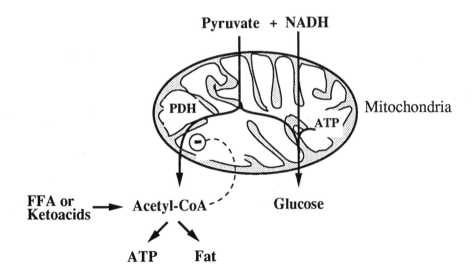

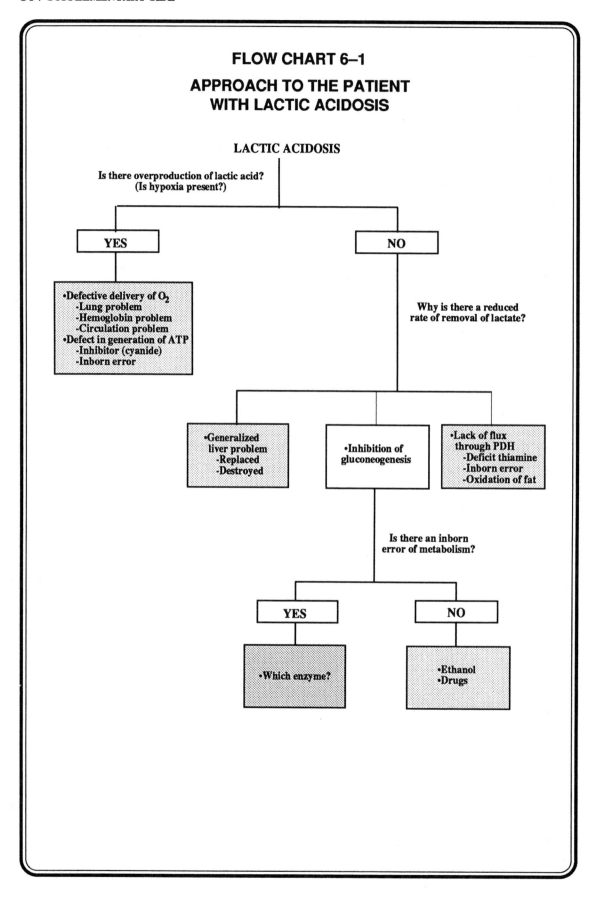

FLOW CHART 6–1

APPROACH TO THE PATIENT WITH LACTIC ACIDOSIS

LACTIC ACIDOSIS

Is there overproduction of lactic acid?
(Is hypoxia present?)

YES

NO

•Defective delivery of O₂
  -Lung problem
  -Hemoglobin problem
  -Circulation problem
•Defect in generation of ATP
  -Inhibitor (cyanide)
  -Inborn error

Why is there a reduced
rate of removal of lactate?

•Generalized
liver problem
  -Replaced
  -Destroyed

•Inhibition of
gluconeogenesis

•Lack of flux
through PDH
  -Deficit thiamine
  -Inborn error
  -Oxidation of fat

Is there an inborn
error of metabolism?

YES

NO

•Which enzyme?

•Ethanol
•Drugs

METABOLIC PROCESSES INVOLVING LACTATE

(Figure 6–3)

Lactic acidosis can be caused by:

1. Overproduction of lactic acid
   - Almost always hypoxia in one or more tissues.

2. Under–utilization of lactic acid, due either to:
   - Reduced flux through pyruvate dehydrogenase (PDH).
     - Hypoxia
     - Oxidation of fat derived fuels
     - Thiamine (vitamin B_1) deficiency
     - Inherited problem with PDH
   - Reduced flux through glucogenesis:
     - Liver damage
     - Excess formation of NADH, as in metabolism of ethanol
     - Presence of inhibitors such as drugs like phenformin.

FIGURE 6–3

METABOLIC PROCESSES INVOLVING LACTATE

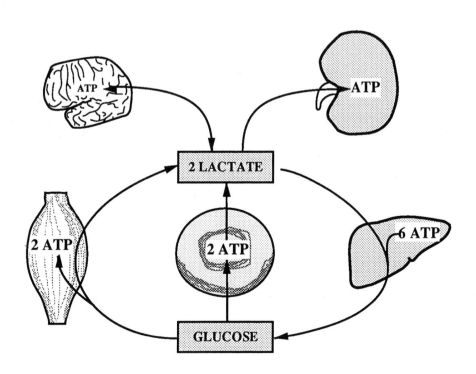

DISCUSSION OF CASE 1:
GARTH HAD A HEART ATTACK

1. Accumulation of Lactic Acid

No. Because overall delivery of oxygen should just be adequate (8 mmol O_2/l) x (2.5 l/min) = 20 mmol O_2/min) and the body needs 15 mmol O_2/min.

2. Need For an Oxygen Mask

Not really; the level of oxygen in his blood is normal. Garth would require oxygen if there was insufficient oxygen in his arterial blood and there was insufficient delivery of oxygen to his tissues.

Perhaps if there is local hypoxia in the heart which is *very* marginal in degree, therapy with oxygen might help. Notwithstanding, this is a minor contribution as only a very tiny fraction of oxygen in blood is carried as dissolved oxygen.

3. Activation of PDH

An activator of PDH will help "select" lactate, rather than FFA, as a fuel to yield ATP. There is a small theoretical advantage of burning lactate vs fat with respect to the yield of ATP per O_2. Each lactate yields 18 ATP and uses 3 O_2 (6 ATP/O_2). With FFA (consider palmitate) 23.5 O_2 are used to yield 129 ATP (5.6 ATP/O_2). Thus if the supply of oxygen is marginal, Garth will need less oxygen to make the requisite ATP by burning lactate rather than fat. This may be important in the areas of his heart with a marginal supply of oxygen.

4. Content of Hemoglobin Blood

If the cardiac output can rise 3–fold, it will be 15 l/min. Since the demand for oxygen is 15 mmol/min, there must be a delivery of 1 mmol of oxygen/l of blood to meet this demand. Since the blood normally contains 8 mmol of oxygen/l, the reduction in hemoglobin must be to less than 1/8 of normal.

Our purpose in providing this example is to illustrate that a low concentration of hemoglobin is rarely the sole cause of lactic acidosis. Loss of blood by hemorrhage will cause lactic acidosis because it also compromises the cardiac output owing to a reduced blood volume.

5. Excessive Anemia and Lactic Acidosis

A reduction in hemoglobin to 25% of normal means that the content of oxygen in blood is now 2 mmol/l. With a cardiac output of 15 l/min, the delivery of oxygen to tissues will be 30 mmol/min. Since the demand for oxygen in this example is 45 mmol/min, there will now be overproduction of lactic acid by anaerobic metabolism.

CASE EXAMPLES

CASE 6–1:
LACTIC ACIDOSIS IN A PATIENT
WHO MAY HAVE HYPOXIA

Garth came to the emergency room complaining of crushing anterior chest pain. You suspects a heart attack.

- On physical examination, his blood pressure is low, his pulse is difficult to palpate and his heart is pumping half as much blood as usual to his tissues.
- His blood contains the normal content of oxygen (8 mmol/l).

QUESTIONS
(Discussion on facing page)

1. Will Garth have accumulation of lactic acid in his blood? (Blood can normally carry 8 mmol of oxygen/l; the normal cardiac output is 5 l/min; the usual rate of oxygen consumption is 15 mmol/min).
2. Should Garth be given an oxygen mask to improve delivery of oxygen to his tissues?
3. What will Garth's response be to administration of an activator of PDH ?
4. How far must the concentration of hemoglobin be decreased before a subject cannot deliver sufficient oxygen to his tissues to match their demand for oxygen?

• Hints:

Tissue demand for oxygen is 15 mmol/min
- Normal cardiac output is 5 liters/min
- Cardiac output can increase 3–fold during hypoxia

5. Would a patient with only 25% of the normal content of hemoglobin present in the blood develop lactic acidosis if he increases his muscular work such that his overall rate of oxygen consumption increases 3–fold to 45 mmol/min?

DISCUSSION OF CASE 6–2:
LACTIC ACIDOSIS
WITHOUT HYPOXIA

1. **Why the lactic acidosis?**

   These are 3 potential causes for reduced delivery of oxygen to the tissues:

   a) **A lung problem.** This can be ruled out if the system for oxygen is normal. In this regard, "Lung doctors" assess the partial pressure of oxygen (P_{O_2}). Since the P_{O_2} was not low, there was no major lung problem.

   b) **A red blood cell (RBC) problem.** No. The concentrations of hemoglobin and oxygen are normal.

   c) **A circulatory problem.** This is not present in this case. There is no problem with the delivery of oxygen. This is lactic acidosis without hypoxia (see Table 6–1).

2. **Number of liver cells.** Give vitamin B_1. The response should be very rapid (hours). If not, damage of the liver is the cause. In general, the damage of the liver would have to be very extensive (80%), given the great capacity of the liver to remove latate.

3 **Activator of PDH.** Yes. An activator of PDH will consume lactic acid providing that either (or both)

   a) There is a need for more synthesis of ATP.

   b) The rate of oxidation of other fuels (fat) for ATP can be reduced.

   • The fuel mixture oxidized can be assessed by examining the respiratory quotient (RQ, the ratio of the production of CO_2 to the quantity of oxygen consumed; an RQ which is < 1 suggests that fat is being oxidized).

   • Replacement of fat with lactate will be beneficial; the potential drawback of this therapy is that there is no control of how much lactate (carbohydrate) will be oxidized via PDH.

     – If this treatment causes hypoglycemia, a patient with liver disease may not synthesize enough ketoacids. Hence the effects of hypoglycemia on the brain will be severe.

     – Furthermore, protein may be mobilized to make glucose. This can cause the loss of a large quantity of lean body mass and a high rate of production of ammonium. The latter may be troublesome because the synthesis of urea will also be compromized in this patient.

   To summarize, if you give the activator of PDH, give glucose as well, once the concentration of lactate falls appreciably.

CASE 6–2:
LACTIC ACIDOSIS WITHOUT HYPOXIA

Greta has cancer of the colon.

- Despite surgery, the cancer has spread to involve most of the liver.
- She has lost a considerable amount of weight and feels somewhat weak.
- Each month, when she arrives at hospital for chemotherapy, blood tests are performed. The concentration of lactate is very high (12 mmol/l, normal 1 mmol/l); the concentrations of glucose and ketoacids are normal. On acid–base analysis, she has a metabolic acidosis, reflecting the elevated concentration of lactic acid in the blood.
- Her circulation was judged to be normal.
- The concentrations of hemoglobin and oxygen are normal in the arterial blood.

QUESTIONS
(Discussion on facing page)

1. Why might Greta have a high concentration of lactate in her blood? Is it due to a low delivery of oxygen?
2. How could you distinguish if this is a problem of an inadequate liver or a deficiency of vitamin B_1.
3. Might Greta have a lesser degree of acidosis if an activator of PDH were given? Are there any drawbacks to this therapy?

DISCUSSION OF CASE 6–3:
LACTIC ACIDOSIS
IN AN ALCOHOLIC

1. **Is lactic acidosis due directly to the ethanol?**

   No. There is no ethanol in the breath (hence the blood). Hence ethanol cannot be causing a high NADH/NAD ratio in his liver to cause accumulation of lactic acid or a diminished concentration of pyruvate and thus impede glucogenesis.

   Is the ketoacidosis due directly to the ethanol?

   Again, no. Ketoacidosis reflects low insulin. Insulin release is inhibited by increased levels of alpha–adrenergics, which result from the poor circulation.

2. **Development of hypoglycemia?**

   Not really. There are ketoacids to provide ATP in the brain. Glucose might be needed to avert hypoglycemia during therapy.

3. **Consideration for therapy?**

   • The circulatory (ECF volume) problems are the major cause of illness. A solution containing sodium chloride should be administered. This should improve delivery of oxygen to the tissues and hence reduce the production of lactic acid.

   • Potassium should be administered to replace losses.

   • Correction of the low ECF volume will lead to a fall in the concentration of alpha–adrenergic hormones, so insulin, in response to the elevated level of glucose in the blood, will become normal. Lipolysis and ketogenesis will decrease. Brain will again become dependent on glucose for ATP. If the previous alcoholism has depleted stores of vitamin B_1, there will be overproduction of lactic acid once the levels of ketoacids are low and brain cells might die from lack of ATP or accumulation of H^+. Hence, vitamin B_1 (thiamine) should be given at the start of therapy.

CASE 6–3:
LACTIC ACIDOSIS IN AN ALCOHOLIC

Steve ingested a large quantity of ethanol over the past week.

- Over the past several days, he vomited on many occasions.
- He now presents to hospital with the following findings:
  - Low extracellular fluid volume (poor circulation).
  - No alcohol is detected on his breath.
  - Lactic acidosis (12 mmol/l), normal value 0.5 – 1.5 mmol/l
  - Ketoacidosis (6 mmol/l), normal value < 0.5 mmol/l
  - Normal concentration of glucose in the blood.

QUESTIONS
(Discussion on facing page)

1. Can Steve have lactic acidosis due to ethanol if ethanol is no longer present in the blood? What about the ketoacidosis?
2. Should you be concerned about development of hypoglycemia?
3. What are the most important considerations for therapy?

FIGURE 6–4

REVIEW OF THE METABOLISM OF ETHANOL

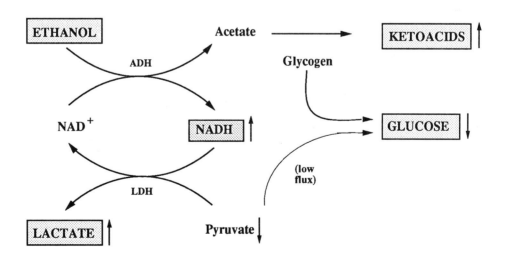

ADH = alcohol dehydrogenase
LDH = lactate dehydrogenase

FLOW CHART 6–2
FACTORS INFLUENCING
THE DEGREE OF KETOACIDOSIS

Ketoacidosis becomes severe if there is an increased rate of synthesis and/or a decreased rate of breakdown of ketoacids. In the ketotic phase of fasting, the total rate of production of ketoacids in one day exceeds the usual ketoacid pool size by close to 10–fold. Metabolism of ketoacids in the brain consumes almost half of the ketoacids produced.

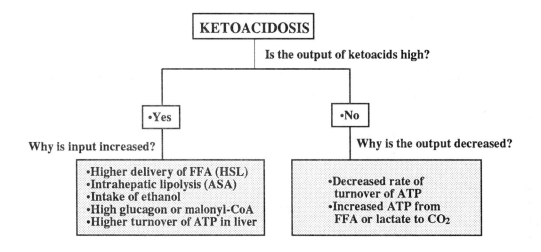

| KETOACIDOSIS |
| Is the output of ketoacids high? |

•Yes   •No

Why is input increased?   Why is the output decreased?

•Higher delivery of FFA (HSL)
•Intrahepatic lipolysis (ASA)
•Intake of ethanol
•High glucagon or malonyl-CoA
•Higher turnover of ATP in liver

•Decreased rate of
 turnover of ATP
•Increased ATP from
 FFA or lactate to CO_2

ASA = acetosalicylate (asprin)

KETOACIDOSIS

General Features

- Ketoacids are produced in large quantities in normals after several days of fasting.
- Ketoacids are partially oxidized derivatives of fat.
- They are synthesized almost exclusively in the liver.
- The initial stimulus for their formation is a high level of FFA and a low level of insulin, the result of the low level of glucose in the circulation during fasting.
- The low level of insulin also promotes intrahepatic oxidation of FFA to yield ketoacids.
- Factors influencing the degree of ketoacidosis are shown in Flow Chart 6–2.
- Ketoacids are the primary fuel for the brain in the ketotic phase of fasting. About half of the ketoacids that are synthesized are oxidized in the brain. This spares about 1 kg of lean body mass per day (see Chapter 1).
- Ketoacids are acids. Hence:
  - H^+ accumulate if the ketoacids accumulate.
  - H^+ accumulate if ketoacid anions are excreted in the urine without a H^+ or NH_4^+.
- There is no acid–base problem if ketoacids are formed in the liver and oxidized to CO_2 in other organs (Fig 6–5), or if ketoacid anions are excreted in the urine with NH_4^+ (most) or as the free acids (minor).

FIGURE 6–5

METABOLIC PROCESSES IN KETOACID METABOLISM

For details, see text. Abbreviations are TG = triglycerides, ßHB = ß–hydroxybutyrate, the principal ketoacid.

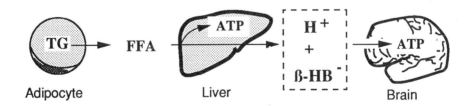

FLOWCHART 6–3
CLASSIFICATION OF KETOACIDOSIS:
ETIOLOGY

Ketoacidosis is caused by a relative lack of insulin. The first step is to assess whether pancreatic ß–cells are normal or damaged. If they are not damaged, either there is a lack of a stimulus for ß–cells or the presence of inhibitors of release of insulin from ß–cells.

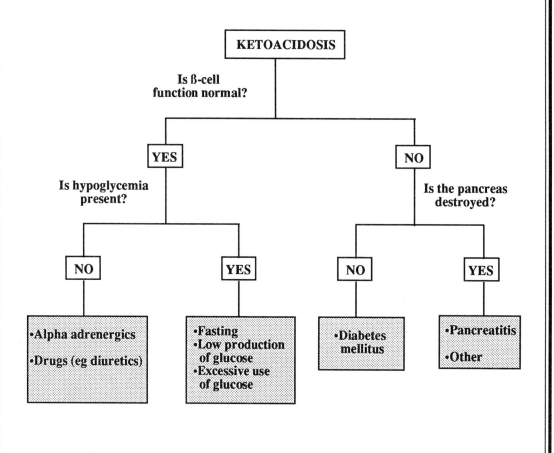

QUANTITATIVE ASPECTS OF KETOACIDOSIS
(see Flow Chart 6–3)

1. Formation

- Extrahepatic factor:
  - Formation of ketoacids is controlled primarily by the concentrations of FFA in the plasma, which in turn respond to the level of insulin (low insulin = high FFA).
- Intrahepatic factors:
  - Low insulin (and high glucagon) also steer FFA in liver cells toward oxidation (and thus ketogenesis) and away from formation of triglycerides (see Chapter 11).
  - The conversion of FFA to ketoacids consumes oxygen (and yields ATP). Hence, the maximal rate of ketogenesis in the liver (close to 2000 mmol per day) is set by the rate of turnover of ATP in the liver. In addition, since other fuels will also be processed by the liver (i.e., conversion of circulating amino acids to glucose or glycogen), the highest rate of production of ketoacids per day is probably closer to 1600 mmol.

- The major considerations in the production of ketoacids are :
  - Synthesized only in the liver.
  - Signal is relative lack of insulin
  - Maximum rate is 1600 mmol/day.

DETECTION OF KETOACID IN THE BLOOD

- The quick clinical test to measure ketoacids detects only acetoacetate (AcAc) and not ß–hydroxybutyrate (ß–HB).
- Ketoacids are linked by an equilibrium reaction:

$$AcAc + NADH \leftrightarrow ß\text{–}HB + NAD^+$$
(detected)   (not detected)

- A high level of NADH will lead to a lower level of AcAc
  - high levels of NADH may be seen during hypoxia (for example, the poor circulation when diabetic ketoacidosis is very severe).
- Hence the rapid test may miss ketoacidosis.

FLOW CHART 6–4:
CLINICAL CLASSIFICATION
OF KETOACIDOSIS

The critical step to assess is whether the patient has a low, normal or high concentration of glucose in the blood.

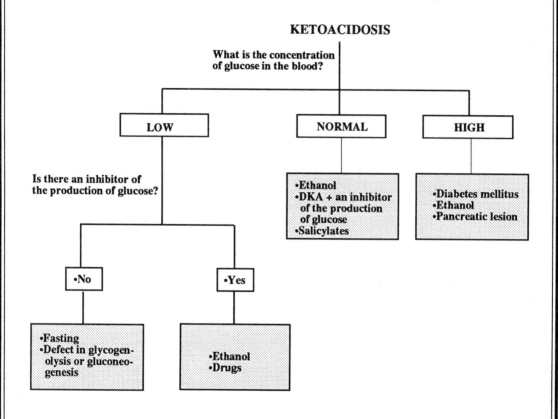

DKA: Diabetic ketoacidosis

2. Breakdown

Removal of Ketoacids Without Metabolism

- One of the ketoacids (AcAc) can be removed by spontaneous conversion to acetone.
  - Protons are removed when AcAc is converted to acetone, which is eliminated via the lungs.
  - Acetone gives the fruity odor to the breath during diabetic ketoacidosis.
  - The production of acetone during chronic fasting is of the order of 100–150 mmol/day, almost 10% of the maximal rate of production of ketoacids.

Removal of Ketoacids by Metabolism

- The major organs which oxidize ketoacids are the brain and kidney.
  - **Brain** The CNS consumes about 500 kcal/day, of which 80% can come from ketoacids during chronic fasting. The CNS therefore can consume about 750 mmol (close to 400 kcal) of ketoacids daily, approximately half the total daily production when there is a lack of insulin.
  - **Kidney** The kidneys both excrete and oxidize ketoacids. Close to 400 mmol ketoacids are extracted per day during chronic fasting: 150 mmol are excreted and 250 mmol are oxidized.
  - **Muscle** Muscle does not oxidize an appreciable quantity of ketoacids during chronic fasting and this helps conserve this essential brain fuel. Muscle consumes FFA for the production of ATP

Possible Modification of The Rate of Utilization of Ketoacids

The rate of consumption of oxygen declines in the brain in diabetic ketoacidosis when the level of consciousness is depressed; it also declines during anaesthesia. In both these states, the degree of ketoacidosis may become more severe because energy demand is reduced and this leads to a lower rate of oxidation of ketoacids.

DISCUSSION OF CASE 6–4:
KETOACIDOSIS
WITH HYPERGLYCEMIA

1. **Blood tests.** The following blood tests would be helpful:

Test	Expected value
Glucose	Very high
Ketoacids	Very high
Bicarbonate	Very low
pH	Very low
P_{CO_2}	Very low

2. **The threats to Andy's life are:**
   - Severe acidosis owing to overproduction of ketoacids.
   - Poor circulation owing to loss of NaCl in the urine.
   - A heart problem related to a low concentration of potassium (usually 1–2 hours after insulin is given).
   - An inadequate quantity of glucose for the brain (usually 6–8 hours after insulin is given), and finally, the underlying illness which provoked the relative lack of insulin.

   Treatment : Treatment will include insulin to stop the production of ketoacids, sodium chloride in water to restore the circulation, and bicarbonate may be necessary if the acidosis is very severe (pH < 7.1 and bicarbonate < 6 mmol/l). Potassium will be needed in the first several hours and glucose should be given once its concentration falls towards 10–15 mmol/l. The underlying illness will also need specific treatment.

3. **The concentration of glucose will fall for 3 major reasons:**
   a) **Dilution,** because the volume of the extracellular fluid will be expanded by solutions which do not contain glucose.
   b) **Loss in the urine.** As the glomerular filtration rate rises, more glucose will be filtered and more excreted in the urine.
   c) **Metabolism:** Oxidation of glucose will only occur once the concentrations of FFA and ketoacids are very low. Hence it takes 6–8 hours before this rate of oxidation can be high. Therefore the "metabolic actions" of insulin to lower the concentration of glucose are delayed.

4. **Coma** will decrease the use of ATP by the brain and thus reduce the oxidation of ketoacids in the brain and cause a much higher level of these acids in the blood.

CASE 6–4:
KETOACIDOSIS AND HYPERGLYCEMIA

Andy, 17 years old, was passing large volumes of urine frequently during the day (polyuria), drinking large volumes of cold beverages because of excessive thirst (polydipsia) and eating excessively (polyphagia); despite this, he was losing weight.

- Today, Andy's mother found that he was confused in the morning, and had became hard to rouse in the afternoon. She called Linda, her doctor, who met Andy and her mother in the emergency room.

- Linda detected the smell of acetone on Andy's breath. She also noted that Andy was breathing very rapidly and deeply. On physical examination, she observed that there was a marked contraction of Andy's extracellular fluid volume (low blood pressure, fast pulse rate).

- Linda suspected that Andy had diabetic ketoacidosis so she ordered specific laboratory tests.

QUESTIONS
(Discussion on facing page)

1. What blood tests do you think are necessary to confirm the diagnosis? What are the expected values? (see Chapter 4 for details)

2. What are the threats to Andy's life? How can they be avoided?

3. After insulin is given, what mechanisms will be responsible for causing the concentration of glucose in the blood to fall early in the course of therapy?

4. Will the fact that Andy is comatose affect the degree of ketoacidosis?

DISCUSSION OF CASE 6–5:
KETOACIDOSIS
IN AN ALCOHOLIC

1. **Why ketoacidosis?**

   • Ketoacidosis is due to relative lack of insulin.

   • Bud need not have diabetes mellitus because there are other possible mechanisms to explain a lack of insulin. For example, the release of adrenaline secondary to the poor circulatory volume will inhibit the release of insulin from ß–cells of the pancreas.

   • This is not the ketoacidosis of fasting because he is hyperglycemic. Thus there must be another reason for the lack of insulin.

2. **Normal concentration of bicarbonate.**

   The ketoacids should have caused acidemia; they did not in this case. Vomiting causes loss of acid. The normal values of pH and bicarbonate in the plasma result because the loss of acid during vomiting equalled the extra acid gained during the accumulation of ketoacids.

3. **Ketoacidosis and a low concentration of glucose.**

   The low concentration of glucose would have two implications:

   a) A low concentration of glucose would result in an absence of a stimulus for the secretion of insulin from ß–cells. This could happen in fasting; however, in this case, the degree of hypoglycemia should be much less marked.

   b) An inhibitor of glucogenesis is present. In this case it is ethanol, acting via the formation of NADH in the cytoplasm of the liver. This is the more likely scenario.

CASE 6–5:
KETOACIDOSIS IN AN ALCOHOLIC
(Fig 6–4)

Bud went on a drinking spree.

- He then felt ill, vomited on many occassions and was difficult to rouse. He was brought to the emergency room by friends who stated that Bud only drank "store–bought" liquor, no unusual liquids (containing methanol, ethylene glycol or isopropyl alcohol). He was not known to have diabetes mellitus.

- Bud only responded to painful stimuli. He had a marked contraction of his extracellular fluid volume and there was a normal rate and depth of respiration.

- Laboratory values for Bud are provided below:

Determination in Blood		Value	(normal value)
Ketoacids	(mmol/l)	8	<1
Glucose	(mmol/l)	20	3.3 – 8
	(mg/dl)	360	60–140
pH		7.40	7.40
Pco_2	(mm Hg)	40	40
HCO_3^-	(mmol/l)	24	24

QUESTIONS
(Discussion on facing page)

1. Why is Bud ketoacidotic? Need he have diabetes mellitus? Could this be ketoacidosis of fasting because he has not eaten for several days?

2. Why does Bud have normal blood values for pH, PCO_2 and HCO_3, yet high levels of ketoacids?

3. Might the cause of the ketoacidosis be different if his blood glucose were 2 mmol/l (very low)? What would be responsible for this very low concentration of glucose in his blood?

DISCUSSION OF CASE 6–6:
MORE ON THE
METABOLISM OF ETHANOL

- The guiding principle is that no more ATP can be synthesized than was hydrolyzed in an organ.
- Since the overall rate of synthesis of ATP in the liver is approximately 18000 mmol/day, the initial metabolism of ethanol cannot provide more than this quantity of ATP, as this component of its metabolism must occur in the liver.
- If ethanol can meet all the needs of the liver for ATP, no other fuel may be oxidized to produce ATP in liver.

1. Metabolism of Ethanol to Yield 18000 mmol ATP

The amount of ethanol that can be consumed by the liver per day depends on the product of its oxidation.

Product	mol ATP per mol ethanol	mmol ethanol oxidized to yield 18000 mmol ATP	g ethanol used per day
Acetate	6	3000	138
CO_2	16	1125	52
ß–HB	3.5	5143	237

Vmax of Alcohol Dehydrogenase (ADH)

- The maximum velocity of ADH will permit a normal subject to oxidize about 275 g (6000 mmol) of alcohol per day. This number is close to the measured value observed when ßHB is the product of the metabolism of ethanol.

2. Clinical Test For Ketoacids

- The clinical test for ketoacids measures AcAc but not ß–HB.
- If a subject had a high NADH/NAD ratio in the liver, most of the ketoacids would be in the form of ß–HB rather than AcAc; hence the clinical test will not detect them (see equation on the facing page).
- A high NADH/NAD will occur because ethanol is being metabolized or if the rate of consumption of NADH is low in mitochondria (hypoxia for example).

CASE 6–6:
KETOACIDOSIS IN ACUTE
ALCOHOL INTOXICATION

> - An organ cannot burn fuels faster than required to meet its demands for ATP.
> - The metabolism of diverse fuels such as ethanol is initiated only in the liver.
> - Synthesis of ketoacids in the liver produces ATP and responds to levels of FFA in the blood, up to a limit imposed by the needs of the liver for ATP.

- A patient is brought to the emergency room after vomiting profusely. He reeks of alcohol, is confused and has marked contraction of his ECF volume.
- The lab report shows a high level of blood ß–hydroxybutyrate and an apparently low level of acetoacetate and acetone.

Overview of Ethanol Metabolism

- Ethanol metabolism *always* yields ATP; the daily turnover of ATP in the liver is close to 18000 mmol
- **Ethanol** $\rightarrow$ **Acetic acid + 6 ATP**
- **Ethanol** $\rightarrow$ **CO_2 + 16 ATP**
- **Ethanol** $\rightarrow$ **$^1/_2$ ß–hydroxybutyrate (ß–HB) + 3.5 ATP**
- Alcohol dehydrogenase in the liver can oxidize 6000 mmol of ethanol per day.

Interconversion of Acetoacetate (AcAc) and ß–Hydroxybutyrate

$$AcAc + NADH + H^+ \leftrightarrow \text{ß–HB} + NAD^+$$
(detected)   (not detected on quick clinical test)

QUESTIONS
(Discussion on facing page)

1. How much ethanol would be metabolized per day if the product was (i) CO_2, (ii) acetic acid or (iii) ß–HB ?

2. Why might the quick clinical test for ketoacids not be positive in this patient?

DISCUSSION OF THE QUESTION

- By consuming 1350 kcal/day, this subject can burn only 150g of fat (9 kcal/g).

- Since the molecular weight of palmitate (a typical FFA with 16 carbons) is close to 250, then 150 g of palmitate is equivalent to 600 mmol (150000 mg/250).

- The stoichiometry is one palmitate (C_{16}) yields 4 ketoacids (C_4).
  - Thus, the maximum possible rate of production (and utilization) of ketoacids per day is 2400 mmol (4 x 600 mmol).
  - Hence a rate of 3600 mmol/day is not possible.
  - This requires that fat supply all the ATP in the body and that all organs use ketoacids as their principal fuel.

- The other quantitative problem is that of the rate of turnover of ATP in the liver.
  - The metabolism of palmitate to ketoacids must occur in the liver.
  - It yields close to 30 mmol of ATP per mmol FFA; 600 mmol of palmitate will yield 18000 mmol ATP. This equals the rate of turnover of ATP in the liver.
  - Hence there is also a turnover problem for energy in the liver, if the rate of ketogenesis had to be >2400 mmol/day.

CONCLUSIONS

1. The data suggesting a rate of ketogenesis of 3600 mmol/day seem to be incorrect.

2. Values of 1500 mmol/day underestimate the rate of production of ketoacids as the GI tract uses ketoacids as a fuel (probably 100–200 mmol/day during the ketotic phase of fasting). A rate of 1500 mmol/day implies that some ATP is synthesized from other fuels in the liver (FFA to CO_2, protein to glucose etc).

3. For other fuels to yield more ATP in the liver, the rate of synthesis of ketoacids must decline or the rate of turnover of ATP in the liver must rise (more work must be done by cells of the liver).

KETOACODOSIS
(continued)

QUESTION
(Discussion on facing page)

- Is the rate of production of ketoacids "without meals" more likely to be 1600 or 3600 mmol per day ?

Principles

> - No more ATP can be made than is used in any organ.
> - In the ketotic phase of fasting, the body oxidizes fat for almost all of its production of ATP.
> - A quantitative analysis is required to understand what is really happening.

Background

- There are 2 major types of methods to measure the rate of synthesis of ketoacids during the ketotic phase of fasting.
  - In the first, the concentrations of ß–HB plus AcAc are measured in arterial and hepatic venous blood. The A–V difference in concentration is multiplied by the rate of blood flow to the liver (and the GI tract), yielding a net rate of production of ketoacids of 1500 mmol/day.
  - A second method uses a steady state infusion of radio–labelled ketoacids. From changes in their specific activity, the rate of production of ketoacids is estimated to be 3600 mmol/day.
- Judging from your knowledge of the rate of expenditure of energy (subjects chronically fasted expend 1350 kcal/day), which method is more likely to provide results that are correct?

FIGURE 7–1
DESCRIPTION OF ENZYME ACTIVITY

NORMAL KINETICS

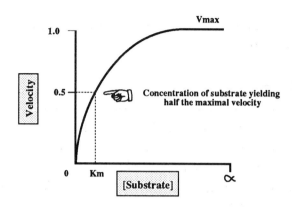

SIGMOID KINETICS

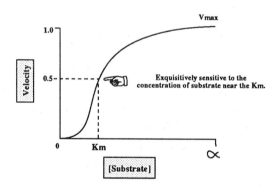

Terminology

1. Definition by the Enzyme

   Vmax: The maximum velocity which can be observed with a fixed amount of enzyme.

2. Definition by the Substrate

   Km: The concentration of substrate which will permit the velocity to proceed at half the Vmax.

3. Definition by the Shape of the Curve

   Michaelis–Menten: The shape of the curve is hyperbolic (top).
   Sigmoid The shape of the curve is sigmoid (bottom).

CHAPTER 7

CONTROL MECHANISMS

HOMEOSTASIS AND CONTROLS OVER PATHWAYS

- Homeostasis requires controls over metabolic systems. These controls are likely to be self–limiting
  - Stimulation by substrates (positive feed–forward) {stimulation by a substrate of its own use ((Fig 7–1)}
  - An increased concentration of a substrate causes the reaction using it to accelerate, thus minimizing the increase in concentration, and vice versa.
  - Inhibition by products (negative feed–back) (inhibition by a substance of its own formation)
  - A decreased concentration of a product causes the reactions forming it to accelerate, thus minimizing this decrease, and vice versa

Changes in Concentration of Metabolites

- Controls over rates of pathways are exerted through concentrations of metabolites acting on an enzyme
  - Metabolites can be fuels, metabolic intermediates, inorganic ions, or anything
- Each intermediate is part of a sequence of reactions
  - Its concentration reflects the balance of its rates of formation and removal
  - Changes in concentration result from relative changes in rates of formation and/or removal

Enzymes Where Control is Expected

> **• Control is exerted on non–equilibrium enzymes.**

- Metabolic pathways or processes are sequences of reactions catalyzed by enzymes.
- Though all enzymes can catalyze reactions in either direction, depending on the concentrations of the reactants, pathways and processes are irreversible in vivo; the reverse pathways use different enzymes and different amounts or types of cofactors.
- Within each pathway, some enzymes keep their substrates and products very close to chemical equilibrium whereas others remain far from chemical equilibrium.
  - Metabolic pathways are controlled at reactions that are far from equilibrium; these reactions are irreversible in vivo.

FIGURE 7–2
INTERACTION OF SUBSTRATES AND HORMONES
TO INFLUENCE THE ACTIVITY OF ENZYMES

Activity of key enzymes must be "on " or "off". There is not a direct pathway between these two form of the enzyme. Binding of a metabolite causes a conformational change which leads a better substrate for phosphorylation or dephosphorylation. This view is a speculative one.

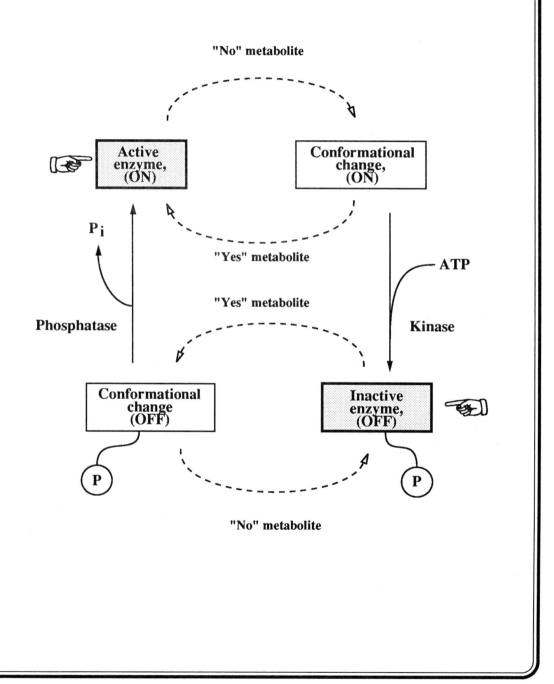

MECHANISMS OF METABOLIC CONTROL

Overview

- Metabolic control results from altering the rates at which enzymes catalyze their reactions.

- Enzymes can be activated or inhibited by three general mechanisms

1. Controls By Activation or Inhibition of Enzymes

- Change the activities of enzyme molecules by changing the concentrations of inhibitors or activators
- Controls are very specific for each enzyme
- Changed concentrations of activators or inhibitors result from other controls
- Responses are instantaneous

2. Controls by Covalent Modification of Enzymes
(Fig 7–2)

- Change the activities of enzyme molecules by modifying them, chemically
- Chemical modifications are most often phosphorylations (adding a phosphate to hydroxyl groups on specific amino acids) or dephosphorylations
- Rates of chemical modification are under their own specific controls
- These controls respond in seconds or, at the most, minutes
- Hormonal controls over enzyme activity usually use this mechanism

3. Long–Term Control

- Change the number of enzyme molecules
- Requires synthesis and/or breakdown of enzyme protein.
- Rates of synthesis and breakdown can be controlled specifically for each enzyme
- These controls usually take hours to respond

FIGURE 7–3
DESCRIPTION OF ENZYME ACTIVITY
(Effect of Inhibitors)

A) Changing the Amount of Enzyme
(non–competitive inhibition)

The family of curves describes events with a constant Km, but the inhibitor causes a decrease in maximum velocity.

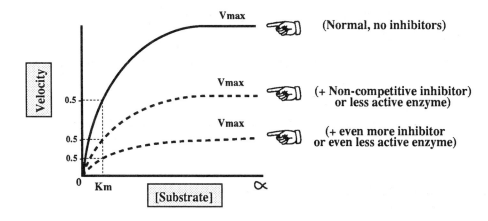

B) Changing the Affinity of Interaction Between Substrate and Enzyme
(competitive inhibition)

The concentration of substrate must rise in the presence of the inhibitor to achieve the same velocity. An excess of substrate can always achieve the same Vmax.

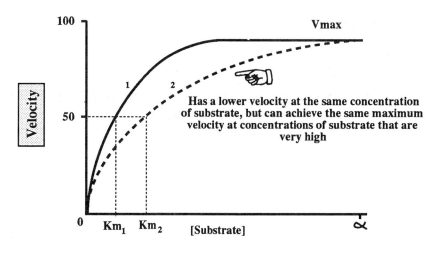

CONTROLS BY ACTIVATION OR INHIBITION OF ENZYMES

Overview of enzyme kinetics

- Consider an enzyme catalyzing the reaction S to P.
- Assume that the enzyme and S are mixed, and there is not yet any P.
- The rate of conversion of S to P will be determined by 3 factors.

1. **Concentration of substrates [S]**

   (Fig 7–1)

   - [S] influences the reaction up to a maximum set by the amount of enzyme.
     - If [S] = 0, rate is 0
     - If [S] is high enough to saturate the enzyme, rate is maximal (Vmax)
     - In between, the rate is determined by enzyme kinetics

2. **Amount of active enzyme (the same as [E])**

   - Changing the amount of enzyme causes the curve in Fig 7–1 to change its vertical scale (Fig 7–3A)
   - This type of control is exerted in all 3 general mechanisms
     - Synthesis and breakdown of enzymes obviously affects [E]
     - Chemical modification can inactivate enzyme molecules
     - Inhibitors can make enzyme molecules inactive{non–competitive inhibition (see below)}
   - Vmax controls offer the possibility of absolute controls over rates in a pathway, irrespective of [S]

3. **Affinity of substrate for enzyme**

   - The Michaelis–Menten equation is based on the assumption that the rate of the reaction depends on [ES], the concentration of the enzyme–substrate complex
   - Changing the affinity of the enzyme for its substrate (Km) changes [ES] with a constant [S]
   - The curve in Fig 7–1 changes its horizontal scale (Fig 7–3B)
   - Km controls do not affect Vmax, but change the rates of reaction at intermediate [S]
   - Km controls tend to occur at branch points in metabolism, or when signals need to be passed up the line

FIGURE 7–4
STRUCTURE OF MEMBRANES

- A phospholipid bilayer forms the barrier.
- Enzymes or other proteins on either side or traversing the membrane allow the communication.

OUTSIDE (ECF)

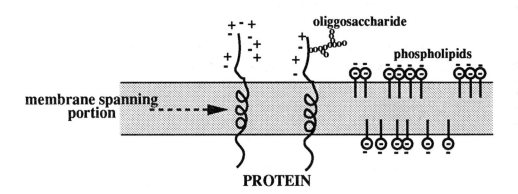

INSIDE (ICF)

Notes:

- The bilayer structure, readily seen in appropriately stained electron micrographs, is approximately 8 nm thick.
- The non–polar central part makes the membrane impermeable to water soluble compounds.
- The phosphate groups (negatively charged) repel soluble anions.
- The enzymes or other proteins in and on the membrane are asymmetrically situated so that the inner surface is very different from the outer surface.
- Functions of surface proteins, in addition to those indicated later, include specific cell–cell recognition, immune mechanisms, and many others.

MEMBRANES AND METABOLIC CONTROL

> • Membranes are both barriers and routes for communication between compartments.

Overview of Membranes
(Fig 7–4)

• All living creatures are made of *cells*.

• Most cells contain *organelles*.

• Cells and organells are all enclosed by *membranes*.

• Membranes are barriers between compartments which may have very different concentrations of intermediates, contain different enzymes and perform different functions.

• Because the compartments must communicate with each other, to work together to allow life, membranes must also provide means of communication between compartments.

Membranes as Barriers

• Cell membranes separate intracellular materials from the extracellular fluid.
  – Different proteins (enzymes inside, plasma proteins (e.g. albumin) outside)
  – Different ion concentrations (30–40–fold gradients for Na^+, K^+, and other ions)
  – The stomach lining can maintain 1,000,000–fold (6 pH units) gradients for $[H^+]$
  – Metabolic intermediates are present only in cells
• Organelle membranes (e.g., mitochondria) perform similar barrier functions.

Membranes as Communication Routes

• Membranes allow
  – Passage of signals from hormones in blood to inside the cell
  – Selective transport of fuels into and out of a cell or an organelle
  – Active pumping of inorganic or organic molecules to achieve concentration gradients
  – Transfer of large molecules (proteins, such as albumen, immunoglobulins, hormones) made in cells to the outside of cells

- **DIFFUSION**
  - Water and lipid soluble, but not repelled by strong ionic groups in the membrane (e.g. – ethanol).

- **CARRIER MEDIATED TRANSPORT**
  - Equilibration transport systems (also called facilitated diffusion)
- Entry of glucose into cells
  - In some tissues, a variant of this transporter is stimulated by insulin.

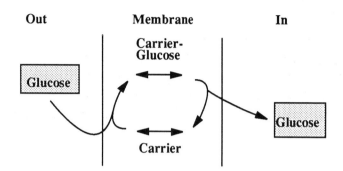

This scheme shows one model. Other models include a specific pore or channel which only allows a movement of specific molecule.

- **ENERGY–DRIVEN TRANSPORT SYSTEMS**

Indirect

- These differ from the above general schemes by linking an energy consuming step (often ATP hydrolysis) to the inside part of the cycle, forcing it in one direction only.

Direct

- Transport of H+ out of the mitochondria during the synthesis of ATP.
- Sodium–linked transporter for glucose in intestine and the kidney
  - Active transport of Na+ out of the cell makes an effective transport for glucose into the cell.

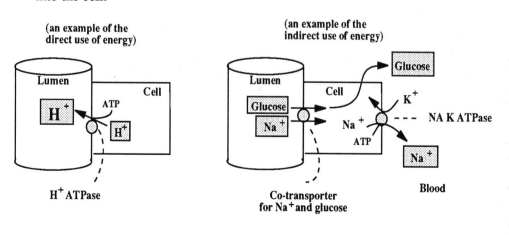

Membranes and Transport

> • Molecules cross membranes by
> - Simple diffusion (uncharged, lipid soluble).
> - Enzyme action, carriers or pores.
> - Membrane fusion (for macromolecules).

Overview

- The membrane barrier is overcome for specific ions, fuels or other small molecules (up to a molecular weight of 300, approximately) by transporting enzymes which are embedded in the membrane.
- The transporters do not change the chemical structures of molecules they carry, but move them across membranes.
- Specificity is as precise as for any enzyme catalyzed reactions.
- Transporters can be of 2 types (see facing page)
  - Equilibrium systems
    - Bring concentrations across the membrane to equilibrium.
  - Energy driven systems
    - Consume energy (usually provided by ATP) to pump molecules against a concentration gradient (e.g. – NaKATPase)
- Transporters of either type may be activated or inhibited by control signals.
- Some transporters of either type carry only one compound; others must carry two compounds in the same direction or in opposite directions.
- Mechanisms of moving large molecules (proteins) or particles across membranes will not be discussed further.
  - These rely on membrane fusion mechanisms

FIGURE 7–5
THE CYCLIC AMP SECOND MESSENGER SYSTEM

Some enzymes are activated by phosphorylation through protein kinase, some are inhibited (see Chapters 8–11). The hormone acts outside the cell by binding to its receptor. The signal is "transduced" through the membrane by a protein called the G–protein (G). This message is transferred to the enzyme adenylate cyclase (AC). When AC is activated, it converts ATP to cyclic AMP (cAMP). Cyclic AMP binds to its receptor which leads to activation of a cyclic AMP–depenent protein kinase (PK$_A$). This leads to phosphorylation of enzymes which activates or inhibits them.

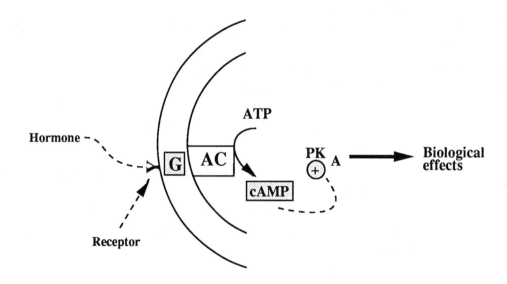

- In general, there are 3 major ways to produce an intracellular message:

1. **Tyrosine Kinase System** The ß–chain of the insulin receptor contains a kinase which phosphorylates tyrosines. One of these tyrosines is on the ß–chain itself (autophosphorylation) and this potentiates this kinase activity. Other proteins are also phosphorylated and this leads to some of the intracellular actions of insulin.

2. **Receptors Interacting With G Proteins** Hormones that lead to the production of cyclic AMP do not react directly with the adenylate cyclase itself. Rather, they act through an intermediate protein that binds GTP to be active, the "G–protein".

3. **Receptors With Other Mediators** Examples of this type of signalling include the receptor mediated opening of sodium or chloride ion channels or the production of other small molecules which relay messages.

MEMBRANES AND HORMONE CONTROLS

Overview

- Many hormones control intracellular functions without entering the cell. They react with specific receptors.
- The hormone signal is transmitted by "second messenger" mechanisms.

• Second Messengers

- The most important second messengers are
  - Cyclic AMP (cAMP)
  - Phosphoinositol 1,4,5–bisphosphate (IP_3) and its metabolites
  - Calcium ions

• Hormone–Receptor Interactions
(Fig 7–5)

- Hormones bind to specific receptor molecules on the outside surface of cells
- Hormone–receptor complexes cause synthesis of the "second messenger", inside the cell
- The second messenger binds to specific receptors inside the cell, which modify other enzymes in metabolic pathways (via phosphorylations or dephosphorylations)
- This mechanism of transfer of the hormone signal results in a very powerful amplification mechanism (a cascade of events)

• Characteristics of Receptors

- They must have a high affinity for hormones as the concentration of hormones remain very low in the circulation minimizing their loss in the urine
- The specificity of receptors is very high. Thus related compounds do not bind to these receptors and thereby exert unwanted biological effects
- Binding must be readily reversible. This permits cessation of biological effects once the concentration of the hormone in the circulation falls
- The number of receptors may change due to synthesis, degradation or movement from the cell membrane to an intracellular site
- The affinity of the receptor may change if the receptor undergoes phosphorylation or an allosteric change
- The receptor may be "uncoupled from its transducer"; an example is the intracellular phosphorylation of the ß–adrenergic receptor

FIGURE 7–6
CONTROLS AT METABOLIC CROSSROADS

Energy metabolism centers around 3 intermediates which asre common to a number of pathways. The most important crossroads are at G6P, pyruvate, and acetyl–CoA. These figures outline the controls at these crossroads.

A) Crossroads at G6P

Liver

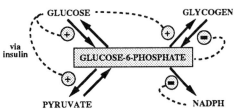

Consumers

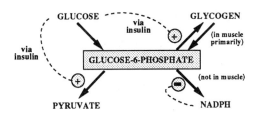

B) Crossroads at Pyruvate

Liver

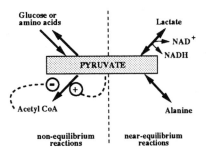

Consumers

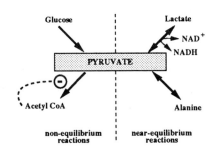

C) Crossroads at Acetyl–CoA

Liver

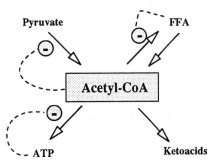

Consumers

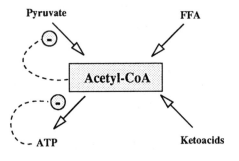

SIGNALS AND THE CONTROL OF ENERGY METABOLISM

> • Signals must be strong enough to elicit on or off messages to pathways.
>
> • Signals are from pathway intermediates, non–pathway intermediates, and via phosphorylations.

• Strength of Signals

– Signals have to be strong enough to fully activate or inactivate a pathway.

  – Can be exerted by the availability of substrate

  – Can be exerted by non–pathway intermediates (pathway intermediates would have to vary over a 10–fold range to be effective; they don't!)

  – Can be exerted by modification of enzymes by phosphorylation (short–term) or by synthesis and/or degradation of enzyme molecules (long–term)

– Signals related to ATP are delivered by AMP in the cytoplasm and ADP in mitochondria as these are the cofactors where concentration can change by an order of magnitude (Table 7–1)

– Other "cousins" or related compounds to ATP can help deliver signals (e.g. citrate)

• Coordination of Signals

– Metabolic intermediates and second messangers from hormones combine to give a "re–enforced signal".

– Enzymes must be on or off (opposite diagonals Fig 7–2).

– Signals are exerted at key crossroads in metabolic processes (Fig 7–6)

TABLE 7–1

CHANGES IN ATP AND AMP IN MUSCLE

The degree of change in AMP is much greater than that of ATP. Hence AMP is a Better signal of "low ATP" in the cytoplasm.

	Rest	Exercise	Change (%)
ATP	7.0	6.3	−10
AMP	0.12	0.26	+116

FIGURE 8–1
THE PATHWAYS OF THE
CARBOHYDRATE SYSTEM

The store, glycogen is in the clear rectangle, the key intermediates are in the inverted triangles and the circulating fuels are in the ovals.

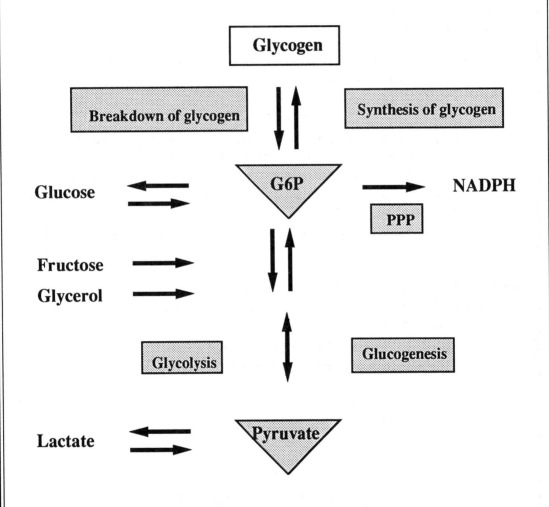

CHAPTER 8

CARBOHYDRATE SYSTEM BIOCHEMISTRY

THE CARBOHYDRATE SYSTEM

An Overview

- The pathways of the carbohydrate system link glucose, glycogen and pyruvic/lactic acids (Fig 8–1).
  - An additional pathway helps generate NADPH for reductive biosynthesis.

Names of Pathways

- **Glycolysis**
  - Splits glucose to pyruvate/lactate

- **Glucogenesis**
  - Converts pyruvate to glucose or glucose 6–phosphate (G6P)

- **Glycogen Synthesis and breakdown**
  - Metabolism of glycogen to and from G6P

- **Pentose Phosphate Pathway (PPP)**
  - Production of reducing equivalents as NADPH for biosynthesis

- **Other Carbohydrates**
  - Energy fuels such as glycerol, fructose and galactose, enter in the middle of glycolysis and glucogenesis.

FIGURE 8–2
GLUCOSE CONVERSION TO ATP
AND CO$_2$ USES 4 PATHWAYS

1. Glucose is converted to pyruvic acid by glycolysis (shaded boxes)
2. Pyruvate dehydrogenase (Chapter 9)
3. The citric acid cycle (Chapter 10)
4. The electron transport chain (Chapter 10).

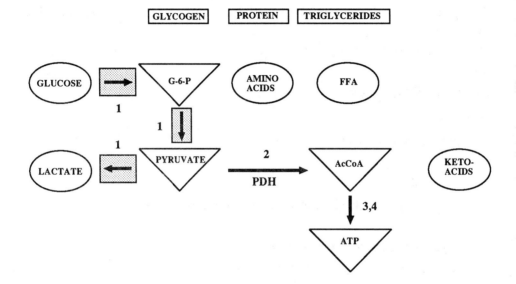

• The overall reaction is shown in equation 5.

$$\text{Glucose} + 6\,O_2 \ \rightarrow \ 6\,CO_2 + 6\,H_2O + 36\,ATP \tag{5}$$

8.1 GLYCOLYSIS

Glycolysis in Perspective
(Fig 8–2)

- Glycolysis can occur in all tissues and uses glucose for 2 reasons:
  1. Synthesis of ATP whenever there is a deficit of ATP

     Glucose $\rightarrow$ **ATP** + carbon products (lactate or CO_2)　　　　　(1)

  2. Synthesis of fat whenever there is surplus of glucose.

     Glucose $\rightarrow$ **Carbon Products (fats)** + ATP　　　　　(2)

Glycolysis and Synthesis of ATP

> - FUNCTION: Make ATP
> - LOCATION: All tissues
> - CONTROL: Product inhibition through ATP (an over-simplification)

- Glycolysis participates in the synthesis of ATP in 2 ways:

1. **Anaerobically**

   Glucose $\rightarrow$ **2 Lactate$^-$ (Pyruvate$^-$)** + 2 H$^+$ + 2 ATP　　　　　(3)

   - The only source of ATP in red blood cells and anaerobic muscle
   - Produces ATP faster than does glucose to CO_2
   - Has a price to pay; it produces acid with ATP. The load of acid can kill!
   - Does not destroy carbon from carbohydrate (pyruvate can be converted to glucose)
   - Control is by feedback by ATP, mediated by related intermediates

2. **Aerobically**

   Glucose + **2 NAD$^+$** $\rightarrow$ **2 Pyruvic acid** + **2 H$^+$** + **2 NADH** + **2 ATP**　　　　　(4)

   - Aerobic glycolysis:
     - Is a source of ATP
     - Participates in the net destruction of glucose because flux continues through PDH
     - Does not yield net acid (pyruvic and lactic acids do not accumulate)
     - Brain requires this pathway for its synthesis of ATP
     - Other tissues will use this pathway if fat–derived fuels are not available
     - Control over this glycolysis is also through feedback by ATP

FIGURE 8–3
CONVERSION OF GLUCOSE TO FAT
USES 4 PATHWAYS

1. Glucose is converted by glycolysis to pyruvic acid (shaded boxes). Pyruvic acid is converted to triglyceride through the pathways of

2. Pyruvate dehydrogenase (Chapter 9)

3. Fatty acid synthesis (Chapter 11)

4. Synthesis and deposition of triglycerides (Chapter 11).

- All these pathways occur in the liver.
  - The liver then "mails" the triglyceride to adipose tissue as very low density lipoprotein, VLDL.

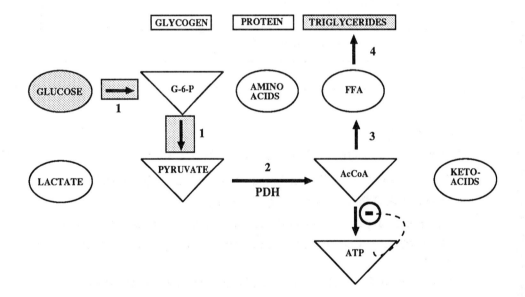

GLYCOLYSIS AND THE CONVERSION
OF GLUCOSE TO FAT

> - **FUNCTION:** Remove surplus glucose
> - **LOCATION:** Liver
> - **CONTROL:** Exerted by the concentration of glucose
>   (through insulin)

- The overall process consists of 4 pathways (Fig 8–3). The glycolysis part of this process is responsible for delivering pyruvate.

- The overall reaction is shown in equation 6

$$\text{Glucose} \rightarrow \text{Triglyceride} + CO_2 + ATP \qquad (6)$$

- Destroys 'glucose–potential' carbon (except for the glycerol part of triglyceride, which is approximately 6% of the carbon of triglyceride).
- Used if there is a large excess of glucose from the diet.
- Is a net producer of ATP.
- Occurs mainly in liver.
- The function of this process is to store carbon from glucose as triglyceride, in times of an excess of dietary glucose.
  - The control systems therefore must override feedback signals by ATP on glycolysis
  - Details of how this feedback control is bypassed will be discussed later in this section
    - Suffice it to say, there is the synthesis of a unique enzyme and a unique activator of glycolysis in the liver
  - Controls are consistent with activation by substrate (glucose) supply acting through fuel–hormone signals

WAYS OF LOOKING AT GLYCOLYSIS

1. **The Overall Pathway**
    *   A 6–carbon molecule (hexose) is split into two 3–carbon molecules (pyruvate or lactate).
    *   All intermediates carry phosphate groups to lock them inside cells and distinguish those being metabolised from those not in the pathway.
    *   Before the 6–carbon molecule is split, it must have a phosphate on either end (one for each 3–carbon molecule.

2. **The Energy Story**
    *   All additions of phosphate at the hexose level require ATP, hence 2 phosphates from ATP are used per glucose.
    *   All additions of phosphate at the triose level require inorganic phosphate (P_i), hence 2 phosphates from P_i are used per glucose.
    *   All 4 bound phosphates yield an ATP on their path to pyruvate. Hence the net yield of ATP is 2 per glucose or 1 per pyruvate or lactate.

    Overall:

    ADP + Triose–P $\leftrightarrow$ ATP + Pyruvate or lactate (7)

3. **The Hydrogen Story**
    *   Each triose yields one NADH upon conversion to pyruvate; this NADH is reconsumed either when lactate is formed or when the reducing power of NADH is transported into the mitochondria for synthesis of ATP.

    Overall:

    $$2\,NAD^+ + Hexose \rightarrow 2\,NADH + H^+ + 2\,Pyruvate^- + H^+$$

    $$2\,NADH + H^+ \rightarrow 2\,NAD^+ + 6\,ATP \qquad (8)$$

GLYCOLYSIS AT THE ENZYME–LEVEL
(A Detailed Look at Glycolsis)

Decide for yourself how few of the steps of glycolysis to memorize to understand its function and control.

INTERMEDIATES	ENZYME	COMMENT
GLUCOSE 1 ⤙ ATP / ADP	1. Hexokinase	Locks glucose in cell
Glucose 6–phosphate 2 ↕	2. Phosphoglucose isomerase	Frees up position 1
Fructose 6–phosphate 3 ⤙ ATP / ADP	3. Phosphofructokinase–1	Adds P to C_1 to prepare for cleavage
Fructose 1,6–bisphosphate 4 ↕	4. Fructose bisphosphate aldolase	Cleavage to 2 C_3P
Glyceraldehyde phosphate 5+ ↕	5. Triosephosphate isomerase	Makes single product
Dihydroxyacetone phosphate 6 ⤙ P_i, NAD / NADH	6. Glyceraldehyde 3–phosphate dehydrogenase	Converts P_i to organic phosphate
1,3–Bisphosphoglycerate 7 ⤙ ADP / ATP	7. Phosphoglycerate kinase	Makes 1st ATP of glycolysis
3–Phosphoglyceric acid 8 ↕	8. Phosphoglyceromutase	Gets next P on correct carbon
2–Phosphoglyceric acid 9 ⤙ H_2O	9. Enolase	Activates ~P
Phosphoenolpyruvate 10 ⤙ ADP / ATP	10. Pyruvate kinase	Makes second ATP of glycolysis
Pyruvate 11 ⤙ NADH / NAD	11. Lactate dehydrogenase	Makes circulating fuel (i.e. lactate)
Lactate		

FIGURE 8–4
THE 3 KEY REACTIONS OF GLYCOLYSIS

- The rate of flow through glycolysis is controlled by the rate of conversion of glucose to fructose–1,6–bisphosphate (F1,6P$_2$), through the first two non–equilibrium enzymes acting as a single system.
- The entry of glucose into the tissue can exert little control.
- The activity of pyruvate kinase has little effect on glycolysis, but is important with respect to the regulation of glucogenesis (Section 8.2).

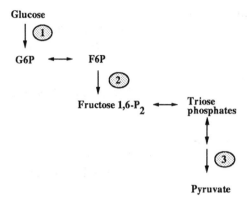

FIGURE 8–5
PROPERTIES OF PFK1

NOTE:

- Citrate inhibits PFK1 in vitro, but citrate concentrations do not seem to change much in tissues, so the physiological significance is questionable.
- When H$^+$ accumulate, PFK1 is inhibited; this prevents an overly rapid rate of accumulation of H$^+$, an accumulation which might destroy the cell or kill the host.

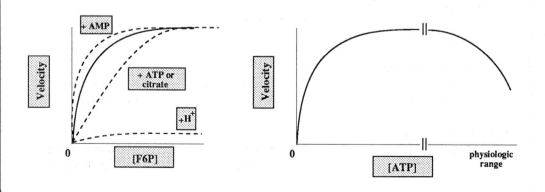

THE CONTROL OF GLYCOLYSIS
(Fig 8–4)

- The rate of glycolysis for the synthesis of ATP is controlled by the activities of hexokinase (HK) and phosphofructokinase–1 (PFK1). These act together as a single control system because G6P inhibits its own formation by HK, non–competitively.
- These controls are over–ridden when glycolysis is used to make fat in liver by inserting a different enzyme to use glucose (glucokinase (GK)) and by adding a new control system over the use of F6P (fructose 2,6–bisphosphate).

- **Key enzymes in glycolysis** 3 reactions in glycolysis are far from equilibrium.

Substrate	Product	Enzyme
Glucose	G6P	Hexokinase or glucokinase
F6P	$F1,6P_2$	Phosphofructokinase–1
Phosphoenolpyruvate (PEP)	Pyruvate	Pyruvate Kinase

1. Control Over Glycolysis to Synthesize ATP

The HK–PFK1 Control System

- HK and PFK1 act as a single system to control the synthesis of ATP in glycolysis
- An increased concentration of ATP can stop use of glucose by HK.
  - ATP inhibits PFK1, competitively; this raises the concentration of F6P.
  - F6P is in equilibrium with G6P; thus G6P rises.
  - High G6P inhibits HK, non–competitively.

a) Properties of PFK1

- Catalyzes the first non–equilibrium reaction unique to glycolysis.
- Is inhibited by ATP, H^+ or citrate and activated by AMP and NH_4^+.
- Inhibition/activation is competitive with F6P (Fig 8–5)
  - PFK1 therefore controls the rate at which a certain concentration of F6P is converted to fructose–1,6–bisphosphate ($F1,6P_2$).
  - Because F6P and G6P are in equilibrium, PFK1 thus controls the concentration of G6P required to achieve a certain flux through PFK1.

FIGURE 8–6
KINETICS OF HEXOKINASE
AND GLUCOKINASE

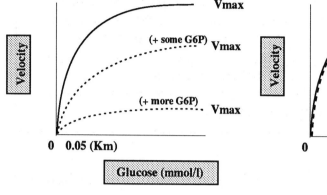

Hexokinase
- Very high affinity for glucose
- Vmax (non–competitive) inhibition by G6P
- Located in all cells except hepatocytes

Glucokinase
- Low affinity for glucose
- Not inhibited by G6P
- Located only in liver

FIGURE 8–7
THE HK–PFK1 SYSTEM AND
THE GK–PFK1 SYSTEM

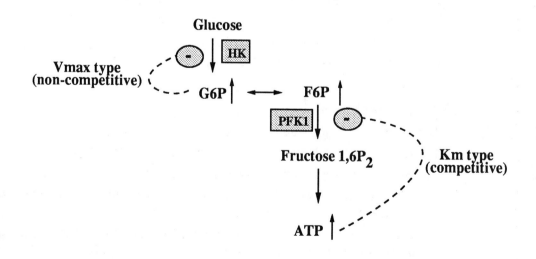

b) Properties of HK

(Fig 8–6)

- Catalyzes a non–equilibrium reaction which allows the entry of glucose into a number of pathways.
- Is inhibited by G6P, non–competitively with glucose (Fig. 8–7).
- Has a very low Km (high affinity) for glucose (Vmax when G6P is 100 umol/l, 2% of the normal concentration of glucose in blood).
- Thus, HK achieves absolute control over entry of glucose into glycolysis.

- The HK–PFK1 control system controls glycolysis in all tissues except liver.
- A high concentration of G6P "says, no appreciable entry of glucose into glycolysis, no matter how high the concentration of glucose".
- Thus the rate of the HK–PFK1 system is independent of the concentration of glucose in blood.

- **The HK–PFK1 system implements the "Golden rule" for between meals:**

  "Burn Fat, not Glucose" if fat is available

---

1. High FFA causes ATP to be synthesized
2. ATP rise causes high F6P (and G6P)
3. High G6P causes no glycolysis until ATP falls

- **Insulin cannot force glycolytic flux by accelerating glucose transport .**
  - A high concentration of glucose in consumer organs cannot overcome the non–competitive inhibition of HK by G6P to any appreciable degree.
  - Insulin accelerates the rate of oxidation of glucose in consumers by depriving them of their supply of "fat fuels".

Properties of pyruvate kinase are described in 8.2, under control of glucogenesis.

FIGURE 8–8
ROLE OF F2,6P$_2$ IN THE REGULATION OF GLYCOLYSIS IN LIVER

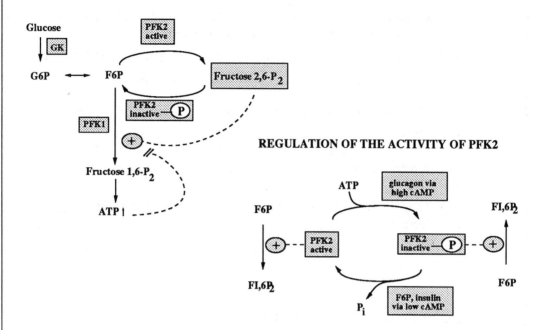

1. **Hormone Signals**
   - High glucose leads to high insulin and low glucagon.
     - These hormones lead to lower levels of cyclic AMP.
       - Low cyclic AMP leads to dephosphorylation and activation of phosphofructokinase–2 (PFK2). The product of PFK2 is F2,6P$_2$, which functions solely as a signal to activate the glycolytic enzyme, PFK1; F2,6P$_2$ is removed by reconversion to F6P.

2. **Substrate Level Signals**
   - F6P is both the substrate and activator for PFK2.
     - Hence high F6P resulting from GK can activate PFK2 and hence PFK1.

3. **Overall**
   - High glucose causes F2,6P$_2$ to rise because of substrate and hormone signals due to surplus glucose acting in concert.
   - High F2,6P$_2$ activates PFK1, despite the presence of ATP
   - This signal system operates primarily in the liver.
   - This control system is the major signal causing a surplus of glucose to be converted to fat.

2. Control Over Glycolysis For Synthesis of Fat

- Liver must convert excess dietary glucose to fat. This process should not be prevented by the presence of high concentrations of ATP. A system is therefore needed to override the strict controls by ATP over HK–PFK1.

- The HK–PFK1 controls are overridden by 2 other enzymes, glucokinase (GK) and phosphofructokinase–2 (PFK2).

Properties of Glucokinase (GK)
(Fig 8–6)

- GK does not have the two major controls of HK.
  - GK is not inhibited by G6P.
  - GK has a high Km for glucose (in the range of the concentration of glucose in the blood during meals).

Hepatocytes (liver cells) contain GK instead of HK. Hence, in hepatocytes, a high concentration of glucose can force its way to G6P irrespective of the concentration of G6P, whereas at low or normal concentrations of glucose in blood, there is not a rapid flow through GK.

Properties of Phosphofructokinase–2 (PFK2)

- PFK1 can be activated by fructose 2,6–bisphosphate ($F2,6P_2$), which is produced by a different enzyme, PFK–2 found primarily in liver.

- PFK2 is activated by energy fuel hormone signals, through high glucose and insulin and low glucagon and cyclic AMP levels.
  - It is also activated by F6P, its substrate.

- The $F2,6P_2$ formed activates PFK1, despite inhibitory levels of ATP (removes ATP inhibition) (Fig 8–8).

FIGURE 8 – 9
EXAMPLES OF TRANSPORT
OF GLUCOSE

1. Metabolic Transport of Glucose

a) Insulin-insensitive

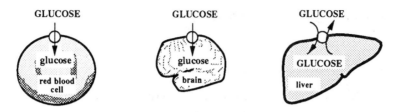

b) Insulin-sensitive

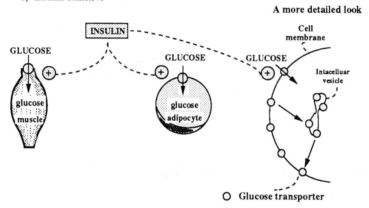

2. Bulk Transport of Blucose
(Intestine, kidney)

This transport uses the gradient for sodium (low in cells due to the active transport of sodium across the basolateral membrane via the NaKATPase).

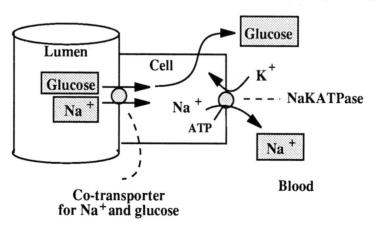

TRANSPORT OF GLUCOSE

- Glucose can only enter cells through a carrier or transporter in the cell membrane.
  - The types of transporters differ between organs
- Most organs require entry or exit of glucose as part of their energy metabolism.
  - This can be called **"Metabolic Glucose Transport"**.
- Intestine and kidney transport glucose into the body from digestion or from the urinary filtrate.
  - This can be called **"Bulk Glucose Transport"** (Chapter 7).

Metabolic glucose transport
(Fig 8 – 9)

a) Some tissues depend heavily on glucose or make it. They have a simple carrier to permit entry of glucose with little or no primary regulation of glycolysis at this step.

- Red blood cells and brain let enough glucose into the cell to meet the needs of glycolysis.
- The transporter for glucose in the brain is in the blood–brain barrier (BBB). The number of active transporters in the BBB changes inversely with the concentration of glucose in the blood to prevent an excessive amount of glucose from entering the brain, leading to damage secondary to non–enzymatic glycosylation or via sorbitol formation with lack of myo–inositol (Chapter 4).
- The transporter in liver allows rapid movement of glucose in both directions as needed. Hence hepatocytes always **"see"** the concentration of glucose in the blood.

b) In certain tissues, use of glucose is optional.

- In muscle and adipose tissue, transport of glucose is controlled by the energy fuel hormone, insulin.
- In muscle, this requirement for insulin is removed when the concentration of ATP in muscle falls – e.g., in anaerobic metabolism of early exercise.
- The large mass of muscle could use an enormous amount of glucose. Hence there must be a tight control on the use of glucose in muscle. This occurs at the HK–PFK1 system.

Bulk Glucose Transport

Glucose must be absorbed from the urinary filtrate and the intestines, often against a concentration gradient. Hence an actve transport mechanism is needed.

DISCUSSION OF CASE 8–1:
HARRY HAD A HEART ATTACK

Problem

- After his heart and brain use their very tiny stores of ATP (and creatine–phosphate), Harry must make all his ATP from anaerobic glycolysis. No fat can be used as its metabolism requires oxygen.

- Anaerobic glycolysis makes one H^+ per ATP.

- **Quantities and time**

- Harry must make as much ATP by glycolysis as he did with oxygen before his heart stopped (72 mmol ATP/min).

- This demands 72 mmol of hydrogen ions per min, which will exhaust the body's buffering capacity in 7 min (Chapter 6).

- The actual survival is shorter, as the brain has a higher requirement for ATP and a lower buffering capacity than organs such as muscle. Also, the brain will quickly run out of glucose as it contains little glycogen.

- **Treatment**

  Get oxygen to his brain. Use cardiac massage, support breathing and hope to "buy time" to reverse his cardiac problem (usually an arrhythmia).

DISCUSSION OF CASE 8–2:
AN HEREDITARY DISEASE

Sugars such as fructose must be converted to glucose in the liver so that other organs can metabolize them. The first step is to convert them to their phosphorylated derivative (which uses ATP), and then to a regular intermediate of glucose metabolism. In hereditary fructose intolerance (HFI), this second step is defective.

There are several unique aspects of the lesion in HFI:

1. Table sugar (sucrose) is **fructose** and glucose.

2. Fructose, the unusual sugar, causes the problem.

3. Problems occurring quickly suggest that these organs take up fructose rapidly, –i.e. the intestines and kidneys which absorb it, and the liver which is the organ that converts a variety of fuels (including fructose) to glucose.

4. Metabolism of fructose to fructose–1–phosphate (F1P) which cannot be used due an hereditary enzyme deficiency, leads to depletion of phosphate, a component of ATP in liver, kidney and intestine, organs with the enzyme necessary to form F1P. These organs develop intracellular problems.

5. Patients with HFI avoid sweets as their ingestion leads to marked discomfort. Consequently, they rarely have tooth decay.

DISEASE EXAMPLES RELATED TO GLYCOLYSIS

CASE 8–1:
HARRY HAS A HEART ATTACK

Harry, a 62 year old male, has had severe crushing chest pain for 6 hours. He went to hospital where his doctor suspected that he was having a heart attack. Suddenly, Harry's heart stops beating. The doctor calls for help and starts to work on Harry.

QUESTION

(Discussion on the facing page)

- How much time does he have before Harry will die ? Explain in biochemical terms. Biochemically, what will save him ?

Hint:

- Think in terms of how organs will generate ATP.
- What is the problem with making ATP without oxygen ?
- What fuel(s) can Harry use to make ATP ?

Necessary Facts For a Quantitative Analysis

- Normal consumption of oxygen is 12 mmol per min and 3 ATPs are formed per atom of oxygen.
- The body can buffer 500 mmol of H^+, acutely, before death.

CASE 8–2:
AN HEREDITARY DISEASE

Some patients develop severe liver, kidney and intestinal problems, very soon after eating when they eat sucrose. Why? You might want to think of it as follows:

1. What is in sucrose?
2. Which component of sucrose is likely to cause the problem?
3. Why do symptoms develop rapidly?
4. Why are the problems restricted to only some tissues, and not brain, for example?
5. What are the dental bills of these patients like?

FIGURE 8–10
METABOLIC PROCESSES INVOLVING
GLUCOGENESIS

Solid arrows indicate the pathways of glucogenesis.

A = GlucoNEOgenesis

B = GlucoPALEOgenesis

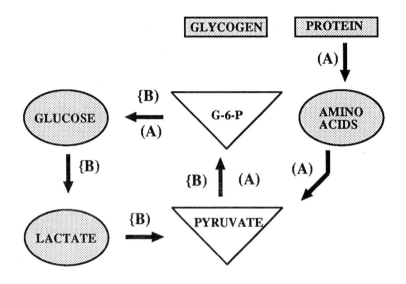

FIGURE 8–11
SOURCES OF GLUCOGENESIS

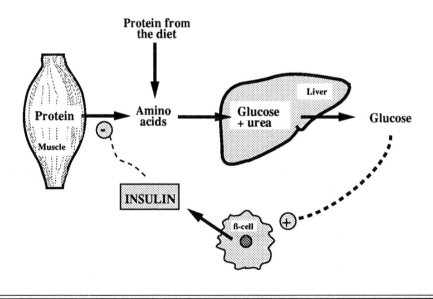

8.2 GLUCOGENESIS

Glucogenesis at the Tissue Level
(Fig 8–10)

- **Pathway**: Glucogenesis is the conversion of pyruvate to glucose.
- **Organ Site**: Glucogenesis can occur in two organs:
  - **Liver**: Glucose is synthesized from protein, lactate, or glycerol (from breakdown of fat stores). Glucogenesis in the liver is the major source of glucose **"without meals"**.
  - **Kidney**: Glucose is produced as a by–product of the metabolism of glutamine which is required to excrete hydrogen ions as NH_4^+ (Chapter 2).
- **Functional Basis:** We identify 2 functional types of glucogenesis.
  1. **Gluconeogenesis.** The synthesis of new glucose from non–glucose precursors (protein, glycogen in muscle).
  2. **Glucopaleogenesis.** The conversion of glucose via pyruvate back to glucose; this leads to net transfer of ATP between tissues.

A) GlucoNEOgenesis

> - A pathway to synthesize new glucose
> - Overall reaction: Protein $\rightarrow$ glucose + ATP + urea

- Operates during meals in liver which first sees all the unique fuels (dietary amino acid, Fig 8–11).
- Operates between meals when there is insufficient glycogen in its store to meet the need for glucose. The price to pay is loss of lean body mass.
- Linked to the synthesis of urea to remove nitrogen.
- A relatively low flux pathway.
- Control is by the load of dietary protein "during meals" and by the concentration of glucose in the blood "between meals".
  - This latter is mediated by the energy–fuel hormones.
    - Low insulin and high glucagon lead to high rates of gluconeogenesis and vice versa.

FIGURE 8–12
EXAMPLES OF GLUCOPALEOGENESIS

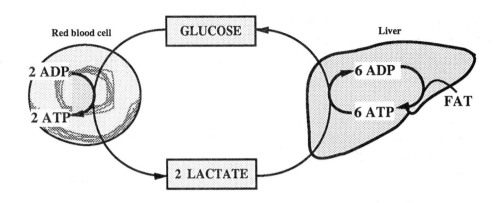

NADH Story
• Glucogenesis can usually be from lactate, amino acids or glycerol.

1. Lactate glucogenesis uses lactate produced in other tissues.
    – Lactate generates its own NADH outside the mitochondrion.
2. Protein glucogenesis uses amino acids either from diet or from breakdown of protein in muscle.
    – The NADH required in gluconeogenesis is carried from the mitochondria via the aspartate used for the synthesis of urea.
3. Glycerol glucogenesis uses glycerol from triglyceride (stored fat).
    – Breakdown of triglycerides occurs "between or without meals".
    – One NADH which is not used in glucogenesis is released per glycerol used.

B) GlucoPALEOgenesis
(Fig 8–12)

> - A pathway to remove lactic acid;
>   - it does not yield "New" glucose

- Glucose is the origin and end of this process.
- Flux depends on the difference between the rate of anaerobic glycolysis (in organs such as the red blood cell) minus the rate of oxidation of lactate.
- Operates "during", "between" and "without" meals.
- Prevents life–threatening acidosis from anaerobic glycolysis in muscle.
- Control is by the delivery of lactate together with the control of the oxidation of lactate in liver via pyruvate dehydrogenase.
- No need for synthesis of urea.
- The implications of the turnover of ATP and NADH on glucogenesis are summarized on the facing page.

> - Overall reaction: an ATP consuming sequence for liver.
>
> **Consumer Organs:** Glucose $\rightarrow$ 2 Lactate + 2 ATP
>
> **Liver:** 2 Lactate + 6 ATP $\rightarrow$ Glucose

Glucopaleogenesis and Muscle

When subjects exercise vigorously, a large amount of glycogen is converted to lactic acid in muscle (Chapter 3). A portion of this lactatic acid can be converted back to glycogen within muscle. This is, in effect, a form of glucopaleogenesis.

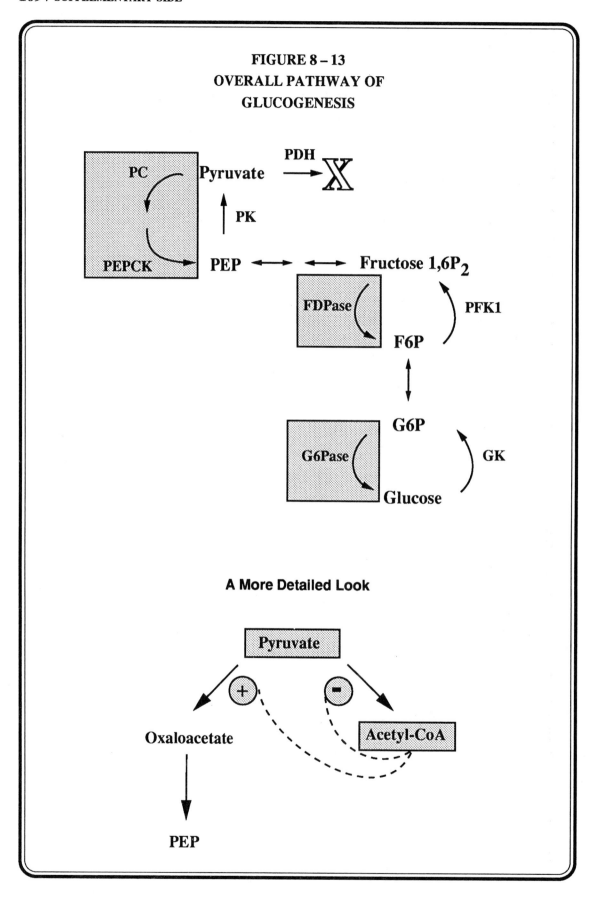

FIGURE 8 – 13
OVERALL PATHWAY OF
GLUCOGENESIS

A More Detailed Look

Glucogenesis at the Enzyme–Level
(Fig 8 – 13)

1. Relation to Glycolysis

- Glucogenesis and the opposing pathway, glycolysis, are closely inter–related:
  - Glucogenesis uses all the glycolytic intermediates, and in the same cellular compartment (the cytoplasm) of the liver.
  - Both pathways use the same near–equilibrium reactions
- The two pathways differ from each other in the enzymes which catalyse non–equilibrium reactions.
  - Pyruvate carboxylase (PC in mitochondria) plus phosphoenolpyruvate carboxykinase (PEPCK in cytoplasm) together oppose the reaction catalyzed by pyruvate kinase (PK)
  - Fructose–1,6–diphosphatase (FDPase) opposes the reaction catalyzed by PFK1
  - Glucose–6–phosphatase opposes the reaction catalyzed by GK
    - Both phosphatases are simple hydrolysis of phosphate esters, opposing the addition of phosphate from ATP

2. Pathways of Glucogenesis

- Gluco**paleo**genesis uses a different pathway from gluco**neo**genesis.
- Gluco**neo**genesis is directly linked to the synthesis or urea, thus disposing of both the nitrogen and the carbon of the amino acid substrates.
- Glucogenesis can be discussed in 2 sections.
  - Formation of PEP + NADH
    - Converts the range of substrates for glucogenesis to the common glucogenic precursors, PEP + NADH, in the cytoplasm
    - Involves both mitochondrial and cytoplasmic enzymes
    - Varies depending on the carbon source
  - Conversion of PEP + NADH to glucose
    - Only extramitochondrial
    - Common to both gluconeogenesis and glucopaleogenesis

DISCUSSION OF QUESTIONS

1. **Proportions of Glucose and Urea**
   - Not all amino acids can yield glucose (ketogenic amino acids); many have more than 3 carbons and there is a 3–carbon stage (PEP) in glucogenesis.
     - Hence only 60% of the weight of proteins are converted to glucose.
     - The usual diet contains 100 g of protein which can yield 60 g (333 mmol) glucose.
     - Protein is 1/6 nitrogen by weight; therefore 100 g protein yield 16 g nitrogen, which is excreted as urea; thus 555 mmol of urea will be synthesized from daily dietary protein.
     - Hence, almost 1.67 mmol of urea are formed per glucose synthesized from dietary protein.

2. **Proportions of PEP and Nitrogen**
   - There are three possible explanations
     a) Some of the PEP could be made from amino acids by a pathway not tied to urea synthesis (i.e. leave the mitochondria as malate).
     b) The urea could recycle. Urea is split in the GI tract to $2\ NH_4^+ + 2\ HCO_3^-$, which return to the liver and join the urea synthesis pathway, enriching the input of nitrogen. Normally close to 25% of urea undergoes hydrolysis in the intestine. This serves a useful function in hibernating bears (see Chapter 2).

     Certain bacteria live below the mucous layer of the stomach. They release urease which generates NH_4^+ a local irritant. This may be involved in the pathogenesis of gastritis (inflamation of the stomach) and in the development of ulcers.
     c) There is more than 1 nitrogen in some amino acids and ketogenic amino acids supply nitrogen but no PEP precursors.

Formation of PEP and NADH in the Cytoplasm

> - Aspartate is the key intermediate.
> - Pyruvate carboxylase is a necessary step.
> - The pathways differ for gluconeogenesis and glucopaleogenesis.

Gluconeogenesis:
- This pathway overlaps with that for the synthesis of urea are identical (Chapter 12)
- Only some of the amino acids are substrates (not the ketogenic amino acids)
  - The substrates are alanine, aspartate and NH_4^+
- PEP and NADH are the first set of products

Glucopaleogenesis:
- This pathway differs from gluconeogenesis (see facing page)
- The substrate is lactate
- The products, PEP and NADH, are formed via different reactions than in gluconeogenesis

Conversion of PEP + NADH to Glucose

> - This pathway is the same for gluconeogenesis and glucopaleogenesis.

- There are two non–equilibrium steps to bypass by the following reactions:
  a) $F1,6P_2 \rightarrow F6P$
  b) $G6P \rightarrow glucose$

Questions to Emphasize Major Points of Gluconeogenesis

1. What are the relative proportions of net glucose and urea synthesized when proteins are metabolized?
2. Urea, PEP + NADH are formed in equimolar amounts in gluconeogenesis.
   - How is this possible if most amino acids have 1 nitrogen per PEP–precursor and urea has 2 nitrogens?

TABLE 8–2
COMPARISON OF GLUCONEOGENESIS
AND GLUCOPALEOGENESIS

	GlucoNEOgenesis	GlucoPALEOgenesis
Substrate	Amino acids	Lactate
Obligatory link to	Synthesis of urea	None
Mitochondrial phase		
– Substrate	Amino acids	Pyruvate
– Carbon product	Aspartate	Aspartate
– Transporter		
– Entry	Amino acid and NH_4^+	Pyruvate
– Exit (major)	Glutamate/aspartate	Glutamate/aspartate + others
Cytoplasmic phase		
– Substrate	Glutamate/aspartate	Glutamate/aspartate + others
– Product	Urea, PEP, NADH	PEP, NADH
Source of cytoplasmic NADH	Malate Dehydrogenase	Lactate Dehydrogenase

Control of Glucogenesis

- The control of glucogenesis has 2 components, the overall body controls, and the biochemical mechanisms in liver deciding between glucogenesis and glycolysis.

Tissue Level Controls

1. **GlucoNEOgenesis**

FUNCTION	CONTROL
• Remove dietary protein	• Load of protein in diet (substrate)
• Make glucose for brain	• Concentration of glucose in blood (product)

There are 2 types of gluconeogenesis

(Table 8–2)

- **"During meals"** gluconeogenesis is controlled by the amount of protein ingested, i.e. positive feed–forward by substrate supply.
- **"Between meals"** gluconeogenesis supplies glucose for brain.
    - It converts all available precursors to glucose whenever the supply of glucose from the diet is inadequate.
    - Its primary rate is determined by the supply of substrates, which is controlled by insulin, which is controlled by glucose, the product of glucogenesis.

2. **GlucoPALEOgenesis**

FUNCTION	CONTROL
• Remove extra lactic acid	• Supply of lactic acid

- Glucopaleogenesis removes lactate from anaerobic glycolysis.
    - The major control is the rate of release of lactic acid from organs other than liver.
        - This depends on
        - The rate of anaerobic glycolysis generating lactic acid.
        - The rate of oxidation of lactic acid for synthesis of ATP in the body.

FIGURE 8–14
SITES OF REGULATION OF GLUCOGENESIS

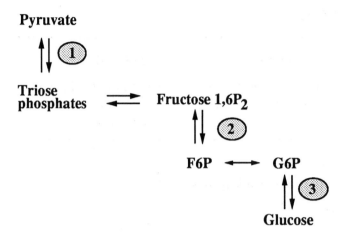

A MORE DETAILED AT PYRUVATE TO PEP

Oxidation of FFA helps promote pyruvate to PEP by inhibiting PDH.

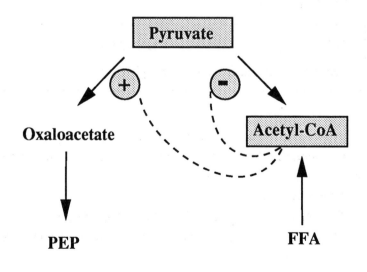

Controls at the Enzyme–Level

> **Overview**
> - Controls over glucogenesis are closely related to those over glycolysis.
>   - Stimulation of key glucogenic reactions is matched by inhibition of key glycolytic reactions, and vice versa.
> - Controls are found in 2 sectors.
>   - Between pyruvate and PEP (major)
>   - Between FDP and glucose (important, but less critical)

Amino Acids to PEP (Gluconeogenesis):

- Main control is by supply of amino acids.
- Pathway is the same as that for the synthesis of urea.
- Enzymes that are regulated:
  - PDH is inhibited by its products, acetyl–CoA + NADH (Chapter 9)
  - Activities of PC, PEPCK and PK are discussed below

Lactate to PEP (Glucopaleogenesis):

- Main control is by the supply of lactate.
- Pathway differs from gluconeogenesis (Fig 8–14)
- Enzymes that are regulated:
  - PDH is inhibited by its products, acetyl–CoA + NADH (Chapter 9)
  - Activities of PC, PEPCK and PK are discussed below

The Pyruvate Crossroads:

(Fig 7–6 and 8–14)

- The key control is at PDH.
  - If flux through PDH is low, glucogenesis proceeds
  - Pyruvate carboxylase (PC) responds directly to the concentration of pyruvate in mitochondria
    - PC is activated by acetyl–CoA, the intermediate which is high when fat if oxidized (and it inhibits PDH).

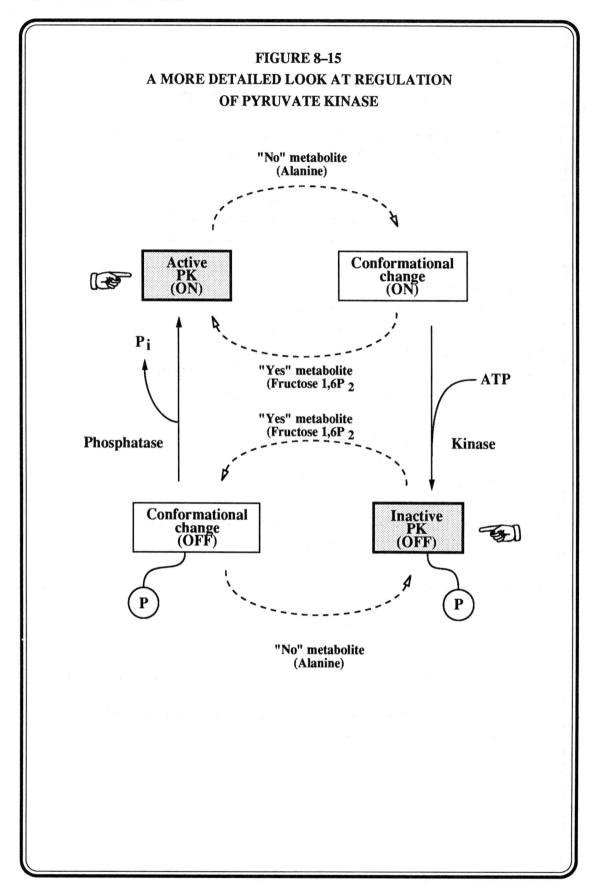

FIGURE 8–15
A MORE DETAILED LOOK AT REGULATION
OF PYRUVATE KINASE

Controls Over PEP to F1,6P$_2$

> • Burn fat and high availability of alanine and lactate are the keys.

- The part of the pathway in the mitochondrion has 2 features:
  - Flux must occur through PC
    - Needs high intramitachondrial acetyl–CoA so is controlled, indirectly, by the supply of FFA.
    - Needs high intramitochondrial pyruvate so PDH must be inhibited and lactate or alanine must be supplied.
- The part of the pathway in the cytoplasm focuses on inhibiting PK (Fig 8–15).
  - Flux through PK is inhibited by
    - Substrates (high alanine and low F1,6P$_2$)
    - Hormones (low insulin, high glucagon signalling that the availability of glucose is low).

Controls Over F1,6P$_2$ to Glucose

> • One main control is by the supply of F1,6P$_2$ from alanine and lactate.
> • The other main control is via inhibition of PFK1 by the low F2,6P$_2$.

- The supply of F1,6P$_2$ was discussed above in that as PEP rises, F1,6P$_2$ rises because they are linked by near–equilibrium reactions.
  - Glycerol and fructose are also converted to F1,6P$_2$
- Regulation is also modulated by the levels of other substrates.
  - e.g. AMP inhibits F1,6P$_2$ase (need abundant ATP for biosynthesis of glucose)
- Glucose 6–phosphatase (G6Pase) has no major regulator, but
  - G6Pase is located in a unique microenvironment and access of G6P to G6Pase may be regulated.

DISCUSSION OF DISEASE EXAMPLES

CASE 8–3:
A PROBLEM WITH GLUCOGENESIS IN LIVER

1. Her problems will be between meals when gluconeogenesis is more critical, she could also be in trouble if she eats a high protein diet.
2. The brain will show signs of lack of ATP between meals unless ketoacids are high.
3. Yes.
    *   Lactic acid will accumulate between meals as a low level of glucose in blood will promote breakdown of protein. She may also have stimulation of breakdown of glycogen in muscle by adrenaline (see Case 1–12).
    *   Ketoacidosis will occur without meals as the low insulin level unleashes hormone–sensitive lipase resulting in high levels of FFA and thereby of hepatic oxidation.
4. No
5. Yes, as this process requires hepatic gluconeogenesis.
6. Blood tests would reveal hypoglycemia, lactic acidosis and ketoacidosis between meals. No enlargement of the liver. Biopsy the liver for enzyme assays.
7. Frequent small feedings and/or a ketogenic diet.

CASE 8–4:
GLYCOGEN STORAGE DISEASE IN LIVER

*   Since the baby did well over the first several weeks of life, seek a lesion in an important, but not critical metabolic pathway. The clues are
    –   Symptoms occur between meals and are relieved by food.
    –   A low level of glucose in blood.
*   Thus the defect should be in the production of glucose.
    –   The most important reaction early in fasting is hepatic glycogenolysis
*   Now consider the big liver.
    –   One would suspect that hepatic glycogen stores are overfilled, but that breakdown of glycogen is impaired.
    –   The most likely lesion is a defect in glucose 6–phosphatase.
*   Therapy Multiple small or continuous glucose feedings through the night.

DISEASE EXAMPLES
(Discussion on facing page)

CASE 8.3:
A PROBLEM WITH GLUCOGENESIS IN THE LIVER

A newborn girl has a problem with low activity of PEP carboxykinase in liver.

1. When will she have symptoms – "during meals" or "between meals"?
2. Which organ will suffer most ?
3. Will she have an acid–base problem ? If so, what will it be ?
4. Will she have a problem oxidizing fat or making ketoacids ?
5. Will she have a problem if the amount of protein in her diet is increased ?
6. How would you make the diagnosis? Describe the characteristic blood abnormalities in the blood?
7. What is your plan for treatment?

CASE 8–4:
GLYCOGEN STORAGE DISEASE IN THE LIVER

A baby fails to thrive after 6 weeks of life. She wakes frequently and is cranky. The mother notes that the baby feels better with each feeding. She also notes that the baby's tummy is protruding more and more. What could be wrong? What will you do about it?

FIGURE 8–16
TURNOVER OF GLYCOGEN IN LIVER
IN THE 24 HOUR CYCLE

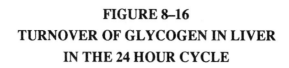

1 = breakfast

2 = lunch

3 = supper

FIGURE 8–17
COMPARISON OF THE FATE OF GLYCOGENOLYSIS
IN LIVER AND MUSCLE

There are 2 points to note. First, the function and therefore the control of glycogenolysis differ between liver and muscle. Second, when glycogenolysis is stimulated, the pathway of glycolysis is inhibited in liver, but activated in muscle.

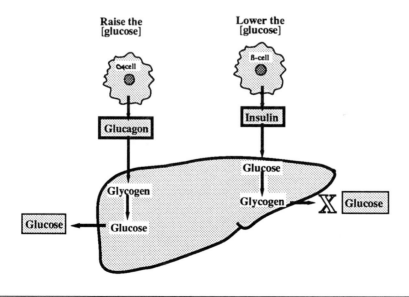

GLYCOGEN

- Glycogen is the direct store for glucose in the body (proteins and glyceride–glycerol are the indirect stores).
- Two tissues, liver and muscle, contain the bulk of the glycogen.
  - Glycogen (in liver) is a reservoir for glucose for the brain
  - Glycogen (in muscle) is a reserve for ATP during rapid vigorous exercise.
- There is a relatively small quantity as glycogen is bulky (it is stored with water)

Glycogen in Perspective

- Glycogen in muscle is the main fate of glucose "during meals"
- Glycogen in liver is the major source of glucose "between meals" ("Glucose Buffer").

Liver

- Glycogen in liver is the major source of glucose for the brain "between meals".
  - Liver contains up to 100 g of glycogen, enough to supply the brain with glucose for 20 hr
  - During meals, glucose from the diet is deposited as glycogen up to a limit set by the number and size of the particles of glycogen (fill the store of 100 g)
    - Control is via a high concentration of glucose and low level of glucagon
  - Between meals, liver releases glucose from its store of glycogen at a rate sufficient to maintain the concentration of glucose in the normal range (Fig 8–16)
    - Contol is via a low concentration of glucose and a high level of glucagon

Muscle

- Glycogen in muscle serves as an energy reserve when the rate of synthesis of ATP is not sufficient to meet the demands for energy in severe exercise (Fig 8–17).
  - Muscle contains close to 20 g of glycogen/ kg (450 g in the average adult)
  - During exercise, glycogen is first converted to G6P and then to lactic acid and ATP
  - Breakdown of glycogen is also stimulated by adrenaline, "the fight or fly response"
  - Stores of glycogen are resynthesized when glucose is available from the diet and use of energy by muscle is low
    - Control is via high concentrations of glucose and insulin, up to a maximum set by the structure and number of the particles of glycogen

- Activation of glycogen synthetase requires that phosphorylase be inhibited (by high glucose in liver).
  - Substrate–level signals reinforce signals mediated by hormone actions.

FIGURE 8–18

THE CASCADE

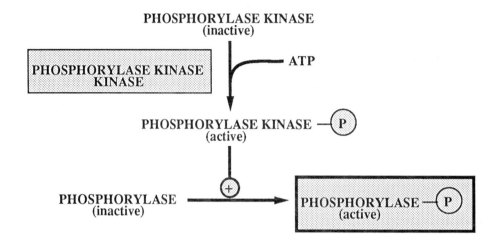

DISCUSSION OF QUESTION

- By osmosis:
  - Not likely because glycogen is a macromolecule, so there are not enough particles
- By binding water:
  - Not likely beacuse only oxygens will bind water
    - Mol wt. glucose (180) is 10 X water (18), so there are 10 waters/glucose if weights are equal
    - 3 g glucose/g water, so 30 molecules of water per molecule of glucose
    - 5 oxygens per glucose in glycogen, so each oxygen in glucose must bind 6 waters

- **Conclusion**
  - We do not how this relationship may occur

Metabolism of Glycogen at the Enzyme–Level
(Fig 8–18)

> • Synthesis and breakdown of glycogen use different pathways.
> • The key reactions are:
>   – Glycogen synthase (synthesis)
>   – Glycogen phosphorylase (breakdown)

• **Synthesis:**

– One key to the synthesis of glycogen is that each glucose must be activated to its UDP–derivative

– The synthesis of glycogen is catalyzed by the enzyme, glycogen synthase, an enzyme that is tightly regulated

– Synthesis of glycogen uses 2 ATPs per molecule of glucose stored

  – 1 to make G6P

  – 1 to make UDP–glucose

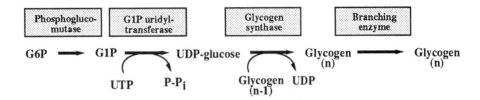

• **Breakdown:**

– The breakdown of glycogen is catalyzed by the enzyme, glycogen phosphorylase, an enzyme that is very tightly regulated

– Inorganic phosphate (P_i) is used in the hydrolysis of the bonds between the units of glucose

– Breakdown of glycogen to glucose does not yield or use ATP

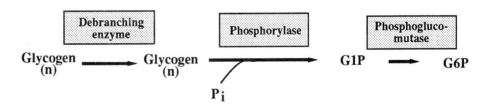

QUESTION
(Discussion on facing page)

How does 1 g of glycogen hold 3 g of water?

FIGURE 8–19
CONTROL OVER THE METABOLISM
OF GLYCOGEN

Raise the [Glucose] in the Blood

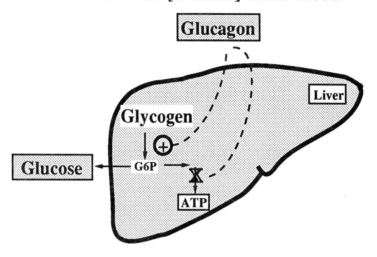

Raise the [ATP] in muscle

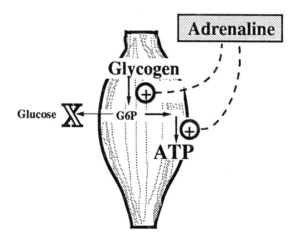

Control of the Metabolism of Glycogen
(Fig 8–19)

> - The activity of phosphorylase is inversely related to that of glycogen synthase.
> - Control involves phosphorylation or dephosphorylation these actions are integrated.
> - Controls are very complex, but operate as a cascade for great effectiveness.

Importance of the Cascade

- Simply controlling the activity of phosphorylase and glycogen synthase directly would not yield the absolute and reciprocal degree of conrol required.
  - Controlling these two enzymes is achieved indirectly, by controlling the activity of other enzymes that phosphorylate or dephosphorylate them (mediate the actions of hormones) (Fig 8–18)
  - This forms a large degree of amplification in regulation, or a cascade
- This cascade:
  - Yields a high degree of amplification of control (1000 X)!
  - Many more enzymes control breakdown and synthesis than actually catalyze these reactions

Breakdown of Glycogen

	FUNCTION	CONTROL	KEY REGULATOR
Liver	Glucose for brain	Blood [glucose]	Glucose, cyclic AMP
Muscle	ATP for muscle in muscle	Turnover of ATP in muscle	AMP, Ca^{++} in muscle

- The functions of glycogen differ in liver and muscle, hence their controls also differ.
  - Control is at phosphorylase, no important controls occur elsewhere.

Synthesis of Glycogen

- Control is exerted at glycogen synthase, no important control occurs elsewhere.
  - Synthesis stops when the store of glycogen is filled
- Since the function of glycogen differs in liver and muscle, regulation also differs.
  - In liver, the most important signal is the concentration of glucose in the portal vein.
    - When this rises to > 7 mmol/l (126 mg/dl), net synthesis of glycogen occurs.
    - Insulin acts by adjusting (downwards) the concentration of glucose that is required to convert the liver from a glucose release mode to one of net uptake.
  - In muscle, most of the glucose removed "during meals" is into glycogen in muscle.
    - The signals relate primarily to the actions of insulin which lead to higher activity of glycogen synthase and a higher level of G6P (accelerated transport of glucose) in the presence of a low level of AMP.

DISCUSSION OF CASE 8–5:
GLYCOGE STORAGE DISEASE
IN MUSCLE

- Muscle is the target.
- ATP is synthesized by two main reactions during anaerobic metabolism.
  - One of them seems to be at fault.
- Acute exercise requires breakdown of muscle glycogen to yield ATP and lactate.
  - The simple test is to exercise anaerobically and see if lactate in venous blood rises appreciably. If it does not, suspect a defect of muscle glycogen phosphorylase. Confirm with a biopsy or do NMR test of muscle cell pH.

1. Hydrolysis of creatine–phosphate (Cr–P)
   - This is extremely rapid.
   - Its hydrolysis consumes a H^+
   - If this were at fault, the muscle would be more acidic and production of lactic acid would yield a higher net load of H^+ upon exercise.

2. Phosphorylase defect in muscle
   - Production of lactic acid and ATP would be inadequate in this case.
   - The concentration of H^+ in muscle cells would be lower than expected
   - Less lactic acid would be found in the venous blood during anaerobic metabolism
   - Levels of phosphorylase would be low in a biopsy specimen of muscle.
   - McArdle found a low tolerance to exercise during anaerobic conditions (sudden bout of exercise)
     - There was a low rate of release of lactate from muscle
     - There was low phosphorylase activity in a biopsy specimen of skeletal muscle .

^{31}P–NMR
The key findings are on initial response to exercise

- Low ATP and high ADP
- Low Cr–P
- Alkaline pH of the intracellular fluid within 3 seconds of exercise.

DISEASE EXAMPLES
(Discussion on the facing page)

CASE 8–5:
JAY HAS A PROBLEM WITH THE
METABOLISM OF
GLYCOGEN IN HIS SKELETAL MUSCLES

Jay, aged 12, suffers from fatigue and painful cramps in his muscles when he performs strenuous exercise.

- Jay is normal in all other respects.

- You suspect that he may have a problem activating the hydrolysis of glycogen in his muscles. (but not in his liver as he does not suffer from a lack of gucose for his brain between meals).

- This disease was recognized by McArdle; how did he arrive at this diagnosis?

- Modern techniques {^{31}P–nuclear magnetic resonance (NMR)} help confirm the diagnosis by measuring the content of ATP, creatine–phosphate, and the pH in muscle cells. How does this information help confirm the diagnosis?

- **Hints:**
  1. Creatine–phosphate + H$^+$ + ADP → Creatine + ATP
  2. Glycogen + 3 ADP + 3 P$_i$ → 2 H$^+$ + 2 Lactate$^-$ + 3 ATP

- **Time course to yield ATP**
  - During exercise, creatine–phosphate supplies ATP for the first 3 seconds, then ATP is derived from anaerobic glycolysis.

SUMMARY OF INTERCONVERSIONS THAT YIELD GLYCOLYTIC INTERMEDIATES FROM PENTOSES

$$C_5 + C_5 \rightarrow C_3 + C_7$$
$$C_3 + C_7 \rightarrow C_6 + C_4$$
$$C_4 + C_5 \rightarrow C_6 + C_3$$

Net: $3\,C_5 \quad \rightarrow 2\,C_6 + C_3$

DISCUSSION OF CASE 8–6

- NADPH can be generated by 3 metabolic pathways
  1. Pentose phosphate pathway
  2. Malic enzyme pathway
  3. NADP–linked isocitrate dehydrogenase.

- The malic enzyme and the NADP–linked isocitrate dehydrogenase pathways require mitochondria so they are not present in red blood cells which depend completely on glucose 6–phosphate dehydrogenase (G6PDH) to detoxify peroxides and to protect hemoglobin from alteration.

- Certain drugs place greater pressure on red blood cells to detoxify peroxides. People with a low activity of G6PDH in cells are prone to lysis of red cells owing to formation of peroxides if they ingest these drugs. This syndrome was first described after the ingestion of the antimalarial drug pamaquine, but many other examples have now been described.

- Deficiency of G6PDH is especially common in blacks where it is a sex–linked trait, and quite frequent among Mediterraneans (e.g. Gino Casetta).

- One hypothesis for such a high incidence is that in some way a deficiency of this enzyme led to a measure of protection against malaria caused by Plasmodium falciparum; perhaps reduced glutathione is required for optimal parasite growth.

- **Summary**
  - The director was right.
- Liver has 2 other ways to make NADPH.
- Muscle has no pentose phosphate pathway so they are not as likely to be affected by a G6PDH deficiency.

PENTOSE PHOSPHATE PATHWAY
(PPP or the hexose monophosphate shunt)

> • PPP generates the type of reducing power (NADPH) required for biosynthesis.

• Two mol of NADPH are generated per mol G6P converted to pentose–phosphate.

• **G6P + 2 NADP$^+$ $\rightarrow$ Ribose 5–phosphate + 2 NADPH + 2 H$^+$ + CO$_2$**

• The rate–limiting step is catalyzed by glucose 6–phospate dehydrogenase (G6PDH).
  – G6PDH is always saturated with its substrate, G6P
  – Control is by the availability of NADP$^+$ (or inhibited by a surplus of NADPH)
• The PPP also catalyzes the interconversion of 3,4,5,6 and 7 carbon sugars in the cytoplasm of cells.
• Because control is through NADPH, the PPP is tightly linked to rates of:
  – Fatty acid synthesis (liver)
  – Detoxification via formation of H$_2$O$_2$ (phagocytosis in white blood cells)
  – Resynthesis of reduced glutathione (in red blood cells, for example).
  – Synthesis of steroid hormones in the adrenal gland.
• Sometimes the carbon product, ribose 5–phosphate is required
  – For synthesis of PR–PP, an intermediate for making purine bases.
• Transketolase requires activated vitamin B$_1$ {thiamine pyrophosphate (TPP)}.

CASE 8–6:
THE PROBLEM WITH BROKEN
RED BLOOD CELLS

While filming a movie in an area endemic for malaria, one actor (Gino Casetta) developed hemolytic anemia ("broken" RBCs).

• The director thought it was caused by the drugs used to prevent malaria whereas the producer said this was unlikely because the two other actors, James Smith and Bob Jones, also took the same medications without ill effects.
• Who was right, the director or producer? Explain you answer.
• Why was the lesion restricted to red blood cells and no pathological consequences were seen in liver or muscle?

FIGURE 9–1
OVERVIEW OF PDH

The process for the conversion of glucose and most amino acids to ATP is shown in the upper diagram. It occurs during meals in all organs and it also occurs in the brain, between meals.

The events in the liver during meals are shown in the lower diagram.

PDH and the Metabolic Process to Synthesize ATP

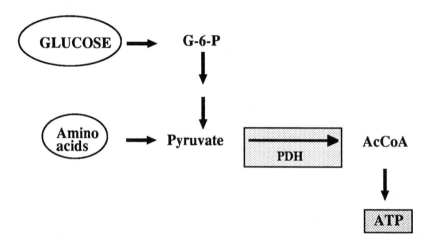

PDH and the Metabolic Process to Synthesize Fat

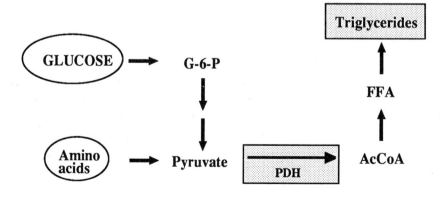

CHAPTER 9

PYRUVATE DEHYDROGENASE (PDH)

> • PDH catalyzes an irreversible reaction.
> • PDH annihilates precursors for carbohydrates.
> • Controls require rapid transitions between the active and inactive forms of PDH so that the activity of this enzyme is *on* or *off*.

PDH in Perspective
(Fig 9–1)

• PDH is found in all tissues with mitochondria.

• We regard the enzyme PDH as a system of its own because flux through PDH destroys the precursors of glucose (carbohydrates and proteins).

  – Flux through PDH converts pyruvate (a precursos of glucose) to acetyl–CoA (a precursor of fat and not glucose), irreversibly.

    – Acetyl–CoA can be converted to ATP or fat, not glucose

• Flux through PDH is high "during meals" when surplus glucose is available.

• Flux through PDH should be close to nil "between meals" in all organs other than the brain unless the levels of ketocids are very high (activity of PDH in brain declines now).

  – Unnecessary metabolism of carbon via PDH shortens survival "between and without meals".

• **Control:** The activity of PDH must be ON at some times and OFF at others.

  – Therefore control must be exerted to permit a large fluctuation in activity

  – Control of PDH occurs at 2 levels;

    – Inhibition of the active form of PDH by its products, acetyl–CoA, NADH and ATP.

    – Inactivation (and activation) of PDH by covalent modification.

  – Consumer organs

    – **Active form of PDH:** Feedback inhibition by its products, acetyl–CoA + NADH

    – **Covalent modification:** Mediated by NADH, acetyl–CoA, and ADP.

  – Maintainer organs

    – Energy–fuels and hormones stimulate PDH in the liver to allow PDH to be in its active form to permit the synthesis of fat despite high levels of NADH, acetyl–CoA and ATP (really, a low level of ADP). Thus controls of the consumer organs are overriden.

FIGURE 9–2
A MORE DETAILED LOOK AT
THE PDH REACTION

- Regulation of the active form of PDH by its products is shown in the figure at the top.
- Conversions between the active and inactive form of PDH are shown in the figure at the bottom.

Inhibition of the Active Form of PDH

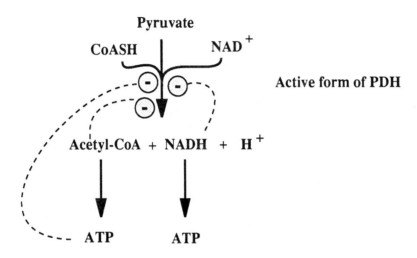

Conversion of Active to Inactive Form of PDH

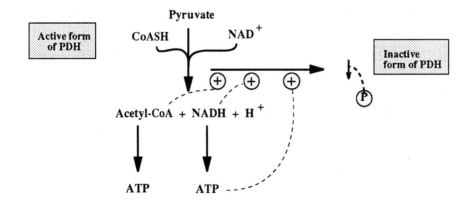

PDH AT THE ENZYME–LEVEL

> • The PDH complex of enzymes catalyzes the conversion of pyruvate to acetyl–CoA.
>
> • The PDH complex also has 2 regulatory enzymes, a kinase and a phosphatase.

• PDH is part of a multi–enzyme complex, containing 5 enzymes and 3 cofactors held together in a single unit.

– Three of the enzymes and all the cofactors are for the reaction,

– Two other enzymes are used in control (the kinase and the phosphatase).

• The PDH reaction requires 2 non–bound cofactors, CoASH and NAD^+, and one further enzyme. A more detailed look at PDH is shown in Fig 9–2.

• **Stoichiometry**

– PDH carries out the net reaction

$$CH_3 - C - CO_2H + NAD^+ + CoASH \rightarrow CH_3 - C - CoA + NADH + H^+ + CO_2$$

(pyruvate)   (Acetyl–CoA)

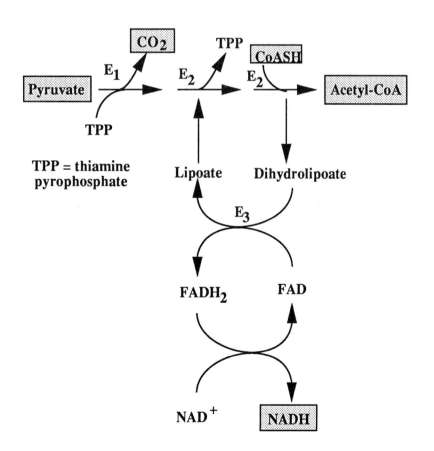

FIGURE 9–3

- The "confirmational change ON" structure is a better substrate for the kinase. This kinasephosphorylates 3 sites and inactives enzyme.
- Insulin leads to an increased activity of PDH phosphatase, and thereby conversion of PDH to its active form.
- This sequential ordering of metabolic intermediates then actions of the kinase or phosphatase provide just one model to explain the events. It is shown as it links substrate–mediated and hormone–mediated actions into a single framework.

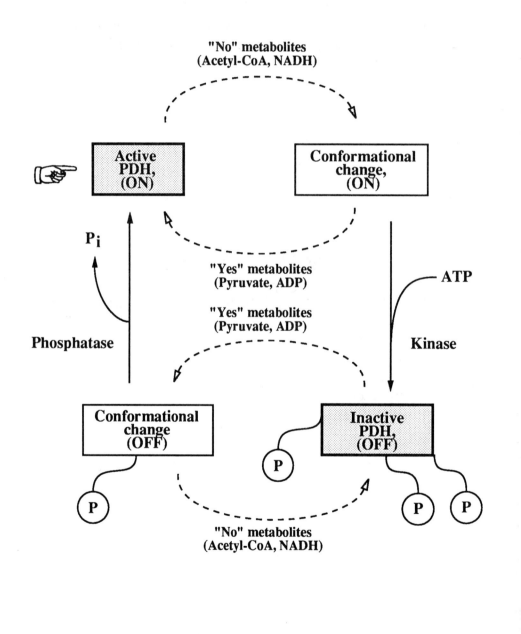

CONTROLS OVER PDH

- In effect, the enzyme is turned on only when needed

- **FUNCTION**
  - Synthesis of ATP
  - Storage of energy as fat

- **CONTROL**
  - Lack of other fuels (FFA) to yield ATP
  - Surplus glucose, via high insulin

A) Consumer Organs
(muscle, brain kidney, Fig 9–2)

- Because PDH cannot be allowed to "destroy" carbohydrate and amino acids unnecessarily, PDH is regulated very tightly. The general strategy is as follows
  - Active form:
    - The active form of the enzyme has a lower activity when its products (the precursors of ATP) accumulate
    - This is not a strong enough stimulus to shut off flux through PDH completely. Hence additional controls occur
  - Inactivation:
    - PDH can be phosphorylated which inactivates it and dephosphorylated, which activates it
    - PDH is converted to its inactive form by a PDH kinase (inactivating PDH)
      - Factors favoring phosphorylation are the same as those that inhibit the active enzyme (low ADP, high acetyl–CoA and NADH)
    - Inactive PDH is converted to its active form by a PDH phosphatase
      - A fall in the concentrations of acetyl–CoA and NADH and a rise in ADP all promote the active form of the phosphatase of PDH, leading to the active form of PDH

B) Maintainer Organs
(liver, Fig 9–3)

- PDH may need to become active so that glucose can be converted to fat, despite the presence of sufficient ATP, NADH and acetyl–CoA. Therefore consumer–type controls must be overridden by mechanisms which activate PDH despite levels of acetyl–CoA, NADH and ATP that are high.
  - All these new controls act via the kinase and the phosphatase.
    - Insulin can lead to the activation of PDH by activating its phosphatase.
    - Pyruvate itself overcomes the inhibition of the kinase of PDH by NADH and acetyl–CoA.

DISCUSSION OF 9–1:
THE BRAIN WAS PICKLED

- The brain can burn glucose or ketoacids.
  - The former requires flux through PDH

- When Jim first arrived in hospital, his metabolism was in the "without meals" mode.
  - He had ethanol to metabolize and thus had an elevated level of ß–hydroxybutyrate
  - Thus his brain derived considerable ATP from the oxidation of ketoacids

- Thiamine (Vitamin B$_1$) is an integral component of PDH.
  - Thiamine is not needed for the usual conversion of ketoacids to ATP (although thiamine is a cofactor for one of the enzymes of the TCA cycle (2–oxoglutarate dehydrogenase), this enzyme is only affected if the deficit of thiamine is very large)

- When glucose was given, the concentration of ketoacids in his blood fell.
  - The brain was dependent on glucose for all of its needs for ATP
  - Should flux through PDH be limited (lack of thiamine), ATP can only be synthesized by glycolysis in the brain

- The areas of the brain with the greatest turnover of ATP or the areas most devoid of thiamine will have a local and lethal overproduction of lactic acid.
  - This damage is called the Wernicke–Korsakoff syndrome
  - If it is even remotely suspected, thiamine should be given in the first bottle of intravenous feeding
  - Thiamine pyrophosphate is also a cofactor for transketolase in the pentose phosphate pathway)

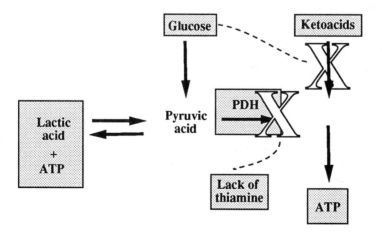

CASE 9–1:
THE BRAIN WAS PICKLED

Jim, a chronic alcoholic, comes to hospital for care.

- He is obviously malnourished.

- While he can carry on a conversation, Jim is obviously confabulating (telling made–up stories lacking a basis in reality).

- Jim has been to the hospital on previous occasions with ketoacidosis due to abuse of ethanol.

  - Jim was given intravenous solutions of glucose on these occasions.

  - Why is this dangerous?

  - What precautions should be taken before he is given glucose in this situation?

- **Hint:**

Think of energy metabolism in his brain.

  - What is Jim's brain using to make ATP before and after the glucose load?

  - What might happen if the levels of ketoacids fell and thiamine (vitamin B_1) is lacking?

SUMMARY OF PYRUVATE DEHYDROGENASE

1. PDH is of crucial importance in metabolism.

    - It catalyzes the irreversible conversion of carbohydrate and protein to fat

2. PDH catalyzes the most tightly regulated enzyme reaction.

    - Flux through this enzyme occurs during meals, and is inhibited by the products of oxidation of fat

> The golden rule concerning PDH is
>
> **"Burn fat to inactivate PDH".**

3. The normal regulation of PDH in consumer organs is overridden in the liver by signals related to a surplus of glucose (insulin, pyruvate).

FIGURE 10 – 1
OVERVIEW OF THE TCA CYCLE

The main function of the TCA cycle is to provide NADH and $FADH_2$ for the synthesis of ATP.

- The substrate that is burned is acetyl–CoA
- The catalysts are 4–carbon intermediates

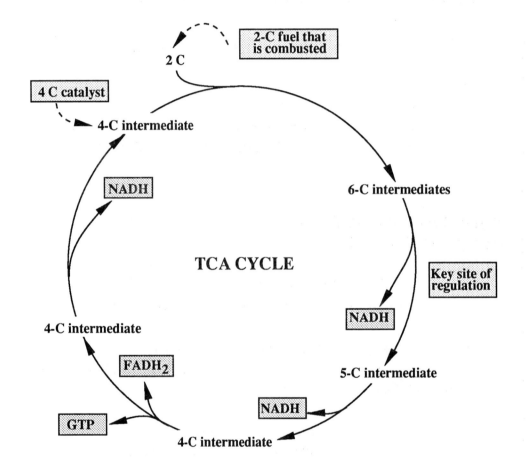

CHAPTER 10

THE ATP GENERATION SYSTEM

OVERVIEW
(Fig 10–1)

> - The ATP generation system contains two pathways.
> - Both are in mitochondria:
>   - The tricarboxylic acid (TCA) cycle to make NADH + FADH2
>   - Oxidative phosphorylation (oxphos) to transfer electrons to O_2 and capture energy as ATP.

The synthesis of ATP has 2 requirements

1. **Source of energy**
   - Electrons are removed from acetyl–CoA and captured by carriers (NAD^+, FAD).
   - The pathway is called:
     - the citric acid cycle (its starting intermediate is citrate)
     - The tricarboxylic acid cycle (because citrate has 3 carboxyls) or
     - The Krebs cycle (after its discoverer Hans Krebs).
   - Components of this pathway are used for other purposes as well (Fig 10–2).

2. **Conversion of some of that energy to ATP**
   - An enzyme complex on the inner aspect of the inner mitochondrial membrane converts the electrons in NADH etc to energy. It:
     - Transfers electrons along a chain of carriers to oxygen, forming H_2O.
       - Pumps H^+ out of mitochondria against both chemical and electrical gradients. This generates potential energy.
       - Allows these H^+ into mitochondria to drive the synthesis of ATP.
   - The pathway is referred to as oxidative phosphorylation because oxidation is linked to phosphorylation.

Quantities
- The vast majority of the ATP is made through the ATP generation system.
  - A small amount more is made by glycolysis.
  - 3 ATP are captured per atom of oxygen or 6 ATP/O_2. In 24 hours, close to 20 mol of O_2 are consumed, yielding 120 mol of ATP, yielding 900 kcal.
  - Although 2000–2400 kcal are ingested, synthesis of ATP captures approximately 50% of this energy.

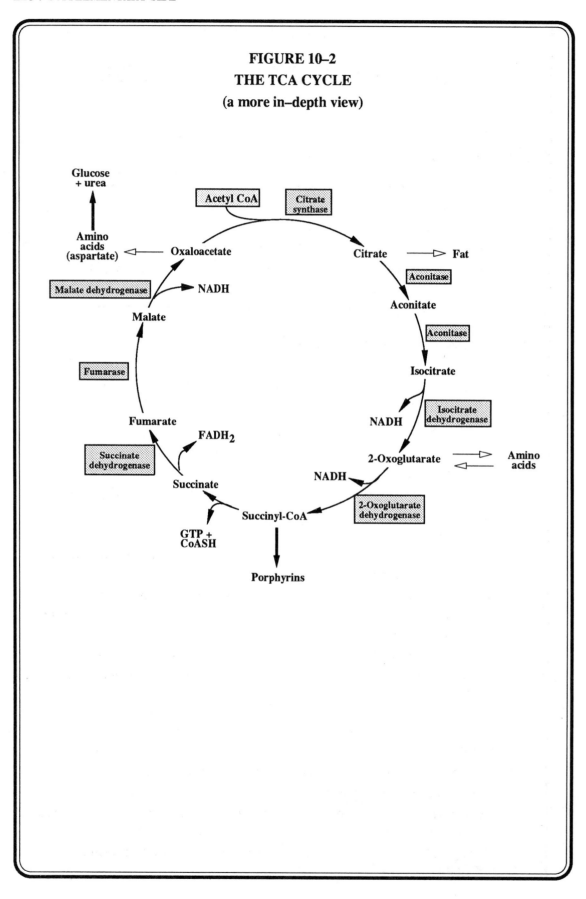

FIGURE 10–2
THE TCA CYCLE
(a more in–depth view)

THE TRICARBOXYLIC ACID CYCLE (TCAC)

> - Produces NADH and $FADH_2$ from acetyl–CoA in mitochondria.
> - The 2 components are a 4–carbon catalyst and a 2–carbon fuel.

TCAC In Perspective
(Fig 10–1)

- The TCAC occurs in all tissues except the few which do not have mitochondria (e.g. red blood cells).
- The overall control for the TCAC is via negative feedback related to the concentration of its major products, NADH and ATP (signalled by its major substrate, ADP).
- The TCAC is also used for other pathways (Fig 10–2).
  - When TCAC intermediates are removed for other pathways, the 4–carbon carrier, oxaloacetate, must be regenerated or the TCAC will stop.
    - Oxaloacetate can be regenerated from pyruvate through pyruvate carboxylase (see Chapter 8), or from the glucogenic amino acids.
  - Conversely, when 4 carbon intermediates are added to the TCAC (oxidation of glutamine, glucogenesis), a pathway which destroys 4–carbon intermediates is also required. Examples are:

    Phosphoenolpyruvate carboxykinase: OAA $\rightarrow$ PEP (Chapter 8)

    The malic enzyme: Malate $\rightarrow$ pyruvate (Chapter 11)

- B–vitamins are cofactors in steps of the TCAC {thiamin (B_1) in 2–oxoglutarate dehydrogenase (very similar to PDH), niacin (B_2) in NAD, flavin (B_3) in FAD}.

TCAC at the Enzyme–level
(Fig 10–2)

- The TCA cycle oxidizes 2–carbon groups to CO_2 and NADH.
  - It functions by adding the acetyl groups to the 4 carbon carrier, oxalacetate, and then taking them off again in stages to regenerate the 4–carbon carrier.
  - In the cycle, 3 NADH, 1 $FADH_2$ and one substrate–level ATP are formed.

- The overall reaction is:

    Acetyl–CoA + 3 NAD⁺ + FAD + GDP + Pi $\rightarrow$ 2 CO_2 + 3 NADH + 3 H⁺ +

    $FADH_2$ + GTP + CoASH

FIGURE 10–3
REGULATION OF THE TCA CYCLE IN LIVER

"**During meals**", there is enough NADH and ATP in liver to meet needs, ICDH is inhibited. Since FFA levels are low, citrate may exit mitochondria and fatty acid synthesis occurs.

"**Without meals**", there is enough NADH and ATP in the liver to inhibit ICDH.

- Now, a high level of FFA stops the exit of citrate
- Acetyl–CoA builds up and leads to the production of ketoacids

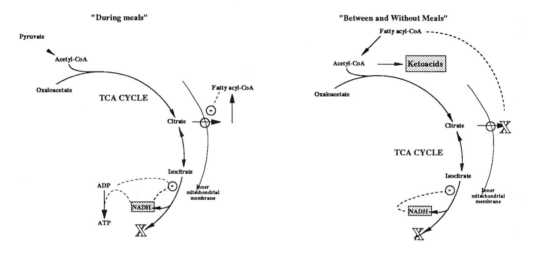

DISCUSSION OF QUESTION
Obtain a High Rate of Synthesis of ATP at a Low P_{O_2}

- Diffusion of O_2 will be faster if the P_{O_2} in mitochondria of muscle is very low.
  - Thus the objective is to keep a low P_{O_2} in mitochondria of muscle
- To obtain maximum flux in the equation below, at equilibrium, the product of the concentration of reactants must exceed that of the products of that reaction.

$$NADH + ADP + O_2 \leftrightarrow ATP + NAD^+$$

- Accordingly, if the concentration of one of the reactants must decline (O_2), there must be a larger rise in the concentration of the other reactants (NADH and/or ADP).
- Because of the controls of the pathway to generate NADH (the citric acid cycle), a very high concentration of NADH occurs when there is a small decline in the concentration of ADP. The net result is a displacement of the equilibrium reaction above to the right.

CONTROLS OVER THE TCA CYCLE
(Fig 10–3)

FUNCTION	CONTROL
• Synthesis of NADH	• Feedback inhibition by NADH, activation by ADP.

• The purpose of the TCAC is to produce NADH and $FADH_2$, the precursors of ATP.

- These can therefore be regarded as the products of the pathway, and are the most likely means of control (negative feedback).

Two enzymes are considered as sites of regulation

A) Isocitrate dehydrogenase (ICDH)

• ICDH is the major site of control over the TCAC.

- ICDH is inhibited by its product, NADH, and activated by an indirect substrate, ADP.

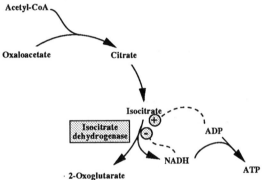

QUESTIONS
(Discussion on facing page)

1. How do you visualize these effectors of ICDH acting in tandem?
2. Can this be advantageous in muscle during exhaustive exercise?

B) 2–oxoglutarate dehydrogenase (OGDH)

• This is an important site of regulation in the kidney as glutamine, the precursor of 2–oxoglutarate, is an important fuel oxidized during acidosis.

• It is also important in the intestinal tract where glutamate is an important fuel.

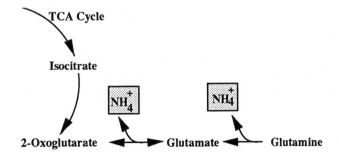

FIGURE 10–4
OVERALL SCHEME OF THE TRANSFER
OF ELECTRONS

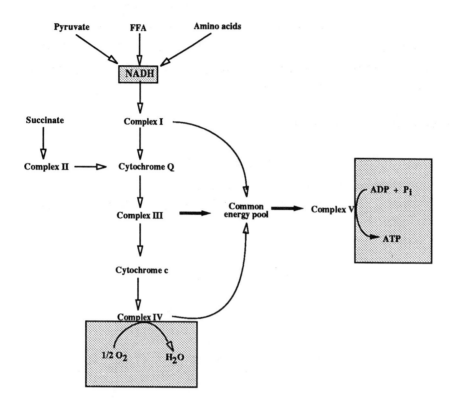

Convincing Experiment Re The Mitchell Hypothesis

- Artificial membranes (vesicles) were made with a concentration of H^+ inside higher than outside.

- An ATPase isolated from beef mitochondria could not synthesize ATP on its own.

- When inserted into the vesicle membrane, ATP was synthesized only if there was an electrochemical gradient for H^+ that was inwardly directed.

Synthesis of ATP

- The concentration gradient for H^+ is used to drive the synthesis of ATP.

- ATP synthase has 2 major components, a proton–conducting unit called Fo and an ATP–synthesizing unit called F_1 or the coupling factor.

  – Protons enter mitochondria through Fo, a hydrophobic, transmembrane protein pore. The F_1 unit is attached to the inner aspect of Fo and catalyzes the reversible interconversion of $ADP + Pi \leftrightarrow ATP$. When H^+ enter the mitochondria through the Fo channel, they bind to F_1, displace ATP, and drive the synthesis of ATP.

ELECTRON TRANSPORT PATHWAY
(Oxidative Phosphorylation)

> - Reduced coenzymes (NADH, FADH$_2$) are oxidized in mitochondria to yield ATP:
>   - 3 ATPs for each NADH
>   - 2 ATPs for each FADH2
> - A proton (H$^+$) gradient is established across the mitochondrial membrane.
>   - Its dissipation is coupled to the production of ATP.

Oxidative phosphorylation (Oxphos) in perspective
(Fig 10–4)

- Oxphos starts with NADH generated in mitochondria.
  - The bulk of NADH (70%) is formed in the TCA cycle, the remainder from formation of acetyl–CoA from the metabolism of glucose, FFA, or amino acids.
    - In liver, much of the NADH is synthesized during the interconversion of fuels.
- A series of carriers takes electrons from NADH (and FADH$_2$) and passes them ultimately to O$_2$.
  - In the process, a large quantity of energy becomes available, mainly at 3 sites.
  - This chemical energy is converted to electrochemical potential energy when H$^+$ are pumped out of mitochondria.
- An ATPase (or ATP synthase in vivo) drives the synthesis of ATP from the energy derived from re–entry of H$^+$ into mitochondria.
  - If H$^+$ enter mitochondria by another route, ATP will not be synthesised.
    - This is called "uncoupling of oxidative phosphorylation.
- The basis for the chemi–osmotic hypothesis is discussed on the facing page.
- Because the purpose of the pathway is to make ATP, it is logical that it should be controlled by feedback by ATP. There is controversy over the details of this control.

Transport of ATP Out of The Mitochondrion

- The chemi–osmotic mechanism synthesizes ATP inside the mitochondrion. Most uses for the energy of ATP are outside mitochondria, in the cytosol or the nucleus. A transporter, called the adenine nucleotide translocase in the inner mitochondrial membrane, exchanges ADP (outside) for ATP (inside). There must also be a transport of P$_i$ from outside to inside the mitochondria. This can be achieved by a carrier which exchanges Pi for OH$^-$ ions .

DISCUSSION OF CASE 10–1:
ART HAD HEART SURGERY

- Lower the rate of consumption of oxygen
  - eg. lower the temperature of the body (induce hypothermia) or by general anesthesia.
- Limit work of his muscles (shivering)
  - eg. from breathing or shivering by administering a drug like curare while performing artificial respiration.
  - Keep the glomerular filtration rate low to lessen the requirement of ATP for the reabsorption of sodium by his kidney.
- Attempt to get more synthesis of ATP per unit of oxygen consumed. The oxidation of carbohydrate will yield at least 6 mol of ATP per mol of oxygen, whereas oxidation of fatty acids provides 7% less ATP per mol of oxygen consumed (see Case 2–3, page 41). This preferential oxidation of carbohydrate can occur if pyruvate dehydrogenase is active.

DISCUSSION OF CASE 10–2:
THE GENERATION OF HEAT

Strategy
- Use a mitochondria–rich tissue.
- Insert a proton channel in the inner mitochondrial membrane which is not linked to the synthesis of ATP (uncoupled oxidative phosphorylation).

Location
- Place this organ around central blood vessels to provide heat where blood can deliver it to the central core organs.

Regulation
- To link function and control, activate these tissues by cold or by the flight–and–fight hormone, adrenaline. Another activator or permissive factor would be an excess of fuel to burn such as fatty acids.

You have just described the physiology and biochemistry of brown adipose tissue, which is found in infants and in animals which can hibernate.

CONTROL OF OXIDATIVE PHOSPHORYLATION

- There are 3 potential controls for oxphos:
  - Supply of NADH
  - Supply of O_2
  - Concentration of ATP (the same as supply of ADP)
    - The signal for ATP in mitochondria is via a change in the concentration of ADP (in the cytoplasm, this signal is mediated by a change in the concentration of AMP).
1. NADH never runs out.
2. Supply of O_2 can be limiting, especially in tissues that can obtain ATP anaerobically (muscle in acute exercise).
3. The ratio of $ATP/(ADP \times P_i)$ is the major continuing control over oxphos
   - The mechanism is uncertain.
   - Many scientists regard most of the pathway (up to cytochrome $a–a_3$) as if it were at equilibrium. If so, then the ratio of $ATP/(ADP \times P_i)$ would be directly linked to the $(NADH \times H^+)/NAD^+$ ratio and that of $FADH_2/FAD$.
     - This could exert strong control.

CASE 10–1: ART HAD HEART SURGERY

Arthur underwent cardiac surgery. He will have a limited supply of oxygen to meet his energy needs.

What recommendations can you make to improve the supply of ATP to the organs of his body ?

CASE 10–2: THE GENERATION OF HEAT

Deduce a mechanism whereby an organ will generate an abundance of heat.

Where should it be located in the body ?

How would you regulate it ?

FIGURE 11–1
THE FAT SYSTEM AND THE NUTRITIONAL CYCLE

During meals, the glucose not needed directly for the synthesis of ATP or glycogen ends up in adipose tissue as storage fat (triglyceride).

In the absence of food, this fat is released from its store, and is the fuel from which ATP is made in the rest of the body.

The Fat System During Meals

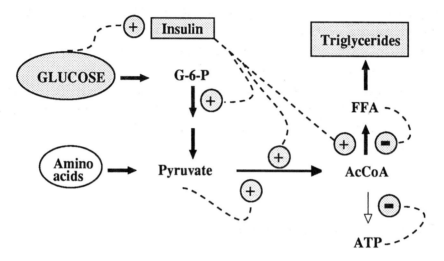

The Fat System Between and Without Meals

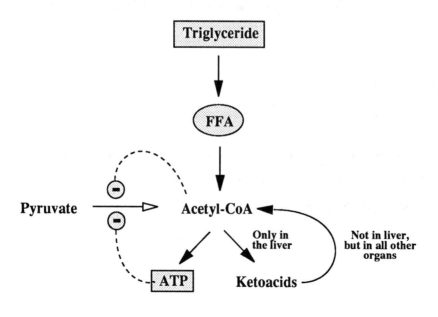

CHAPTER 11

THE FAT SYSTEM

OVERVIEW OF THE FAT SYSTEM
(Fig 11–1)

> - "Between meals", fat supplies almost 100 % of the energy that is needed.
> - "During meals", the metabolic process is storage of fat derived from the diet or synthesized from excess glucose and protein.

- The fat system **"during meals"** uses:

1. **Synthesis of fatty acids**
   - Occurs in liver (mainly), and in adipose tissue
     - This pathway converts surplus glucose and amino acids to FFA

2. **Synthesis of triglycerides**
   - Occurs in liver, and adipose tissue (mainly)
     - Dietary fat is stored as triglycerides in adipose tissue
     - Triglycerides made from glucose or proteins in liver and released as VLDL are stored in adipose tissue

- The Fat System **"between meals"** uses:

   1. Hydrolysis of triglycerides in adipoise tissue.

   2. Oxidation of fatty acids in liver, muscle, kidney and the intestinal tract.

   3. Synthesis of ketoacids in liver.

   4. Oxidation of ketoacids in brain (mainly), kidney and the intestinal tract.

> - Key points of the Fat system:
>   - Synthesis occurs in the cytoplasm and oxidation in mitochondria.
>   - CoASH is a critical cofactor which makes these water–insoluble compounds more water–soluble, locks them in the cytoplasm or mitochondria and participates in the reactions catalyzed by enzymes.

FIGURE 11–2
STAGES 1&2, FORMATION OF EXTRAMITOCHONDRIAL ACETYL–COA

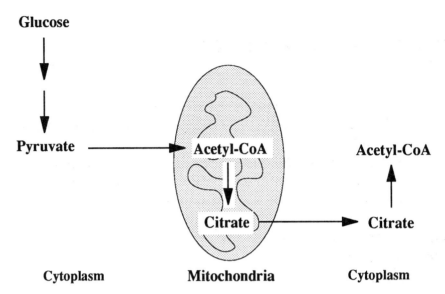

Glucose

Pyruvate → **Acetyl-CoA** → **Citrate** → **Citrate** → **Acetyl-CoA**

Cytoplasm   **Mitochondria**   **Cytoplasm**

STAGE 3, CONVERSION OF ACETYL–COA TO FATTY ACIDS

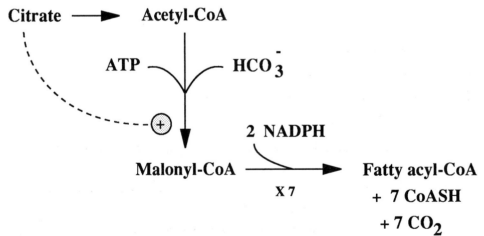

Citrate → **Acetyl-CoA**

ATP — HCO$_3^-$

⊕

2 NADPH

Malonyl-CoA → **Fatty acyl-CoA**
X 7   + 7 CoASH
                + 7 CO$_2$

Details of Reactions of Fatty Acid Synthesis
(complicated, but neat, see Fig 11–5)

FATTY ACID SYNTHESIS

> • Converts surplus glucose or protein to triglyceride in the liver

Fatty Acid Synthesis in Perspective

- **Fatty acid synthesis** (FAS) is active during meals when surplus glucose and amino acids are converted to the efficient storage energy form, triglyceride
- FAS in humans occurs mainly in the liver and to a minor extent in adipose tissue.

Enzymes of Fatty Acid Synthesis

- FAS occurs in the cytoplasm, but its substrate, acetyl–CoA, is generated mainly in mitochondria.
- FAS can be thought of as occurring in 3 stages (Fig 11–2):

   a) The formation of acetyl–CoA in mitochondria via pyruvate dehydrogenase.

   $$\text{Pyruvate} + \text{NAD}^+ + \text{CoASH} \rightarrow \text{Acetyl–CoA} + \text{NADH} + \text{H}^+ + \text{CO}_2$$

   b) The transport of acetyl–CoA out of mitocondria via citrate

   - This reaction sequence also results in the conversion of NADH to NADPH
      - NADH was formed in the cytoplasm along with pyruvate (glycolysis)

   c) The incorporation of acetyl groups from acetyl–CoA in the cytoplasm into long–chain fatty–acyl–CoA and fatty acids (via the fatty acid synthetase complex).

   - An enzyme complex carries out this sequence of reactions
   - Contains the acyl carrier protein (ACP), which links an activated form of acetyl–CoA (malonyl–CoA) to the growing fatty acid chain through the same chemical as in CoA
   - The reaction sequence is shown on the facing page

Overall Stoichiometry

$$\text{Acetyl CoA} + 7 \text{ Malonyl–CoA} + 14 \text{ NADPH} + 14 \text{ H}^+ \rightarrow \text{Palmitate} + 14 \text{ NADP} + 8 \text{ CoASH} + 7 \text{ CO}_2$$

FIGURE 11–3
REGULATION OF ACETYL–COA CARBOXYLASE

$$\text{Acetyl–CoA} + \text{ATP} + \text{HCO}_3 \rightarrow \text{Malonyl–CoA} + \text{ADP} + \text{Pi}$$

- This is an irreversible reaction. It uses ATP and HCO_3 as substrates.
- CoA intermediates are the reactants in the cytoplasm.
- The product is malonyl–CoA, an activated form of acetyl–CoA which is destined for the synthesis of fatty acids (malonyl–CoA is also a key inhibitor of the oxidation of fatty acids).
- **Biotin**, a cofactor, is a B–vitamin. It is involved in all carboxylation reactions.

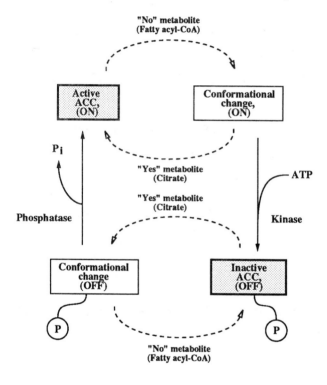

DISCUSSION OF CASE 11–1
ROLLO IS OBESE

Regulation of the synthesis of fatty acids is by a surplus glucose. This supplies more malonyl–CoA to increase flux through the fatty acid synthase complex. Thus if there is no surplus glucose, fatty acid synthetase will not have an increase in substrate to drive its flux. Accordingly, having even 10 X more of this enzyme should not "pull" carbon through the fatty acid synthase complex.

CONTROL OF FATTY ACID SYNTHESIS

> - The primary control is at acetyl–CoA carboxylase (ACC).
> - There are 2 aspects of control, provision of acetyl–CoA in the cytoplasm and activation of ACC.
> - Regulation of ACC is largely via phosphorylation and dephosphorylation.

1. **Provision of Acetyl–CoA to the cytoplasm**
   - **Delivery of acetyl–CoA to the cytoplasm of cells of the liver requires:**
     – A high concentration of glucose to obtain a high flux through glucokinase.
     – A high level of fructose 2,6–bisphosphate to activate glycolysis (Chapter 8).
     – Activation of pyruvate dehydrogenase (Chapter 9).
     – A reduced rate of flux in the TCA cycle (Chapter 10).

2. **Regulation of Acetyl–CoA Carboxylase (ACC) (Fig 11–3)**
   - **Insulin and ACC**
     – Exposure of liver or adipocytes to insulin leads to activation of ACC (persistent).
        – Insulin leads to phosphorylation of ACC, at sites different from those phosphorylated by cyclic AMP (which inhibit ACC).
        – Insulin leads to polymerization and activation of ACC.
        – There appears to be a "tightly bound" stimulator of ACC whose concentration is increased by insulin. This may be one of the phosphoinositol glycans.

   - **Counter–Insulin Hormones and ACC**
     – Exposure of ACC to hormones that increase cyclic AMP lead to phosphorylation of ACC by a cyclic AMP dependent protein kinase and this leads to a marked decrease in activity.
     – ACC is also phosphorylated by 2 cyclic AMP independent protein kinases in the same peptides, but not at the same site as the cyclic AMP induced phosphorylations. These also lead to inhibition.
     – Fatty acyl–CoA augments this phosphorylation and inactivation of ACC.

CASE 11–1:
WHY IS ROLLO OBESE?

Rollo is very obese. A liver biopsy revealed that the level of the fatty acid synthase complex was 10 X normal. Could this be the cause of his obesity?

FIGURE 11–4
INVOLVEMENT OF ORGANS IN ESTERIFICATION

The fuels which will end up as triglycerides in adipose tissue are dietary carbohydrate and fat. The glucose is converted to triglycerides in the liver and exported as a VLDL package containing this triglyceride. Dietary fat is split into FFA (digestion) and converted to triglycerides in the intestine (chylomicrons). All triglycerides in their packages are delivered to adipose tissue where lipoprotein lipase splits them to FFA for uptake in adipocytes.

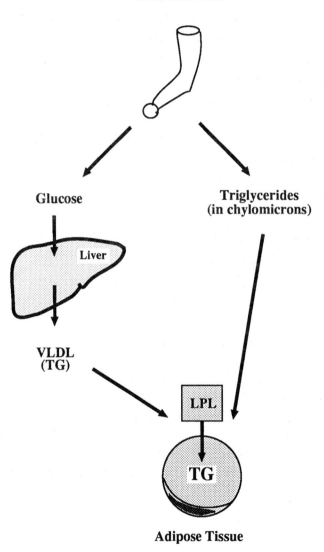

SYNTHESIS AND DEPOSITION OF TRIGLYCERIDES

Synthesis of Triglycerides in Perspective
(Fig 11–4 and 11–5)

> - Triglyceride synthetase converts 3 fatty acyl–CoAs plus glycerol (as alpha–glycerol phosphate produced from glycolysis) to triglyceride.
> - The pathway is controlled by the supply of substrate, i.e., is driven by the same controls as fatty acid synthesis.

- Synthesis and deposition of triglycerides completes the job started by fatty acid synthesis.
- Fatty acids and their CoA derivatives cannot be allowed to accumulate as they are toxic; they act as detergents, destroying membrane structures.
- Synthesis and deposition of triglycerides are active when fatty acid synthesis is occurring.
  - Deposition of triglycerides in adipose tissue occurs when triglycerides are made in the liver or are ingested in the diet.
- Triglycerides that are made in liver are packaged into a "solublized" form (VLDL, very low density lipoprotein). These particles are carried in the blood.
- Triglycerides in VLDL and chylomicrons (the transport form of dietary triglyceride in blood) are stored in adipose tissue.
  - Triglycerides in blood are hydrolysed by **lipoprotein lipase** which produces fatty acids and glycerol in the capillaries of tissues which take up FFA. There are two functional lipoprotein lipases:
  1. During meals, the fatty acids that are released near adipose tissue enter adipose tissue cells and are converted to triglycerides, using alpha–glycerophosphate from glycolysis.
     - The activity of this lipoprotein lipase is increased when the concentration of insulin is high and glucagon is low, in parallel to their effects on the conversion of glucose to fat.
  2. Between meals, the lipoprotein lipase near muscle cells is active and FFA are formed near where they can be oxidized. The activity of this lipase is high when insulin is low and glucagon is high.
     - Lipoprotein lipase is also activated by heparin.

FIGURE 11–5
REACTIONS FOR THE DEPOSITION OF TRIGLYCERIDES

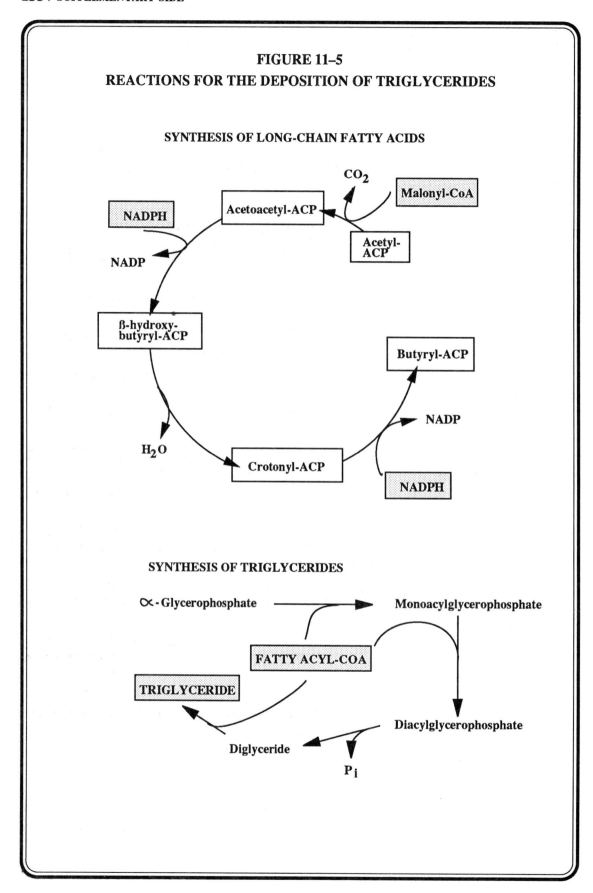

SYNTHESIS OF LONG-CHAIN FATTY ACIDS

SYNTHESIS OF TRIGLYCERIDES

CONTROLS OVER THE SYNTHESIS OF TRIGLYCERIDES

> • Control can exist at 2 levels:
> - Supply of the substrates, alpha–glycerol phosphate and fatty acyl–CoA.
> - Effects on the enzymes of esterification.

• **Control By the Supply of Substrates**

- There are 2 substrates:

  1. Alpha–Glycerol phosphate (derived from intermediates of glycolysis)

  - This was thought to be important at one time, but the rate of esterification can rise markedly without a rise in this intermediate. Hence we do not feel that it is an important regulator

  2. Fatty acyl–CoA

  - The supply of this substrate from fatty acid synthesis in liver and from the products of lipoprotein lipase in adipose tissue is probably the most important regulator

  - Hence, hydrolysis of triglycerides in blood by lipoprotein lipase controls the supply of fatty acyl–CoA and thereby, the synthesis of triglyceride in adipose tissue

• **Control at the Level of Enzymes**

- There are two aspects:

  1. Acute actions of insulin

  - There are no direct actions of any magnitude

  - A 10% activation has been attributed to small molecular weight mediators of insulin action

  2. Long term effects of insulin

  - In fat cells, insulin can increase the levels of all the enzymes involved in the esterification of fatty acids (within 2 hours) (Fig 11 – 5)

  - This appears to involve the synthesis of new enzyme molecules

FIGURE 11–6
RELEASE OF FATTY ACIDS AND
THEIR TRANSPORT IN BLOOD

• Fatty acids are strong detergents. They are the major constituent of soap.

  – They are also rather insoluble at body pH (as very weak acids, they are not dissociated appreciably at pH 7.0)

• Fatty acids are carried in blood bound to serum albumen; only a very small fraction is free in solution.

  – All fatty acids taken up by tissues go through a water–based solution phase

• Fatty acids cross cell membranes by binding to a special membrane protein, the fatty acid binding protein (FABP).

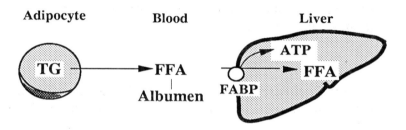

TABLE 11-1
PRINCIPAL EFFECTS OF INSULIN
ON FAT METABOLISM

AT = adipose tissue, L = liver, M = muscle. There are no direct effects on brain.

PROCESS	EFFECT	TISSUE	MECHANISM
1. Fat to ATP	Decrease	AT	• Inhibit HSL (dephosporylation)
	Decrease	L	• Malonyl-CoA inhibits entry of fatty acyl-CoA into mitochondria
	Decrease	M	• Less FFA available
2. FFA to ketoacids	Decrease	L	• Less FFA available • Malonyl-CoA effect • Increase esterification?

HYDROLYSIS OF TRIGLYCERIDES

Breakdown of Triglycerides in Perspective
(FIG 5–6)

> - The major site of control is at hormone sensitive lipase
>   - It is controlled primarily by insulin, which prevents it from being activated.

- The rate limiting step is hormone sensitive lipase (HSL).
  - There may also be some regulation of the exit step where FFA cross the adipocyte cell membrane.
- HSL releases energy fuels (fatty acids) from their most compact store (triglyceride, in adipose tissue).
- The control of HSL must be very sensitive, as it is the tap for the release of energy fuels **"between" and "without" meals**.
  - Control is through the energy–fuel hormones (low insulin leads to an active enzyme).
  - In effect this means that fatty acids will be released if the concentration of glucose is low in the blood.

Hormone Sensitive Lipase

- This is a simple hydrolysis of each of the ester bonds.

$$\text{Triglyceride} \rightarrow \textbf{Glycerol + 3 Fatty acids}$$

Control Over Hormone Sensitive Lipase

- Insulin is the major regulator.
  - Insulin exerts little effect on the basal rate of lipolysis.
  - Insulin inhibits lipolysis that is activated by the hormones adrenaline and ACTH (glucagon has a minor effect on lipolysis).
- Adrenaline and ACTH are the main activators of HSL.
  - They act through cyclic AMP dependent protein kinase.
    - Insulin prevents this action (phosphorylation of serine) by leading to a lower level of cyclic AMP.
    - Insulin may activate a phosphatase.

FIGURE 11–7
METABOLIC PROCESS OF FATTY ACID OXIDATION

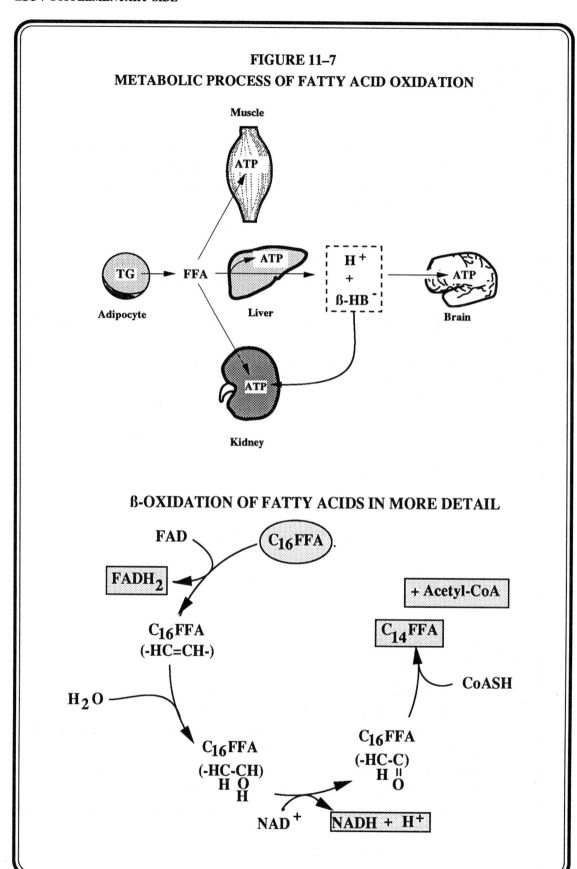

OXIDATION OF FATTY ACIDS

Oxidation of Fatty Acids
in Perspective

> • Fat provides virtually all the ATP for the body "Between" and "Without Meals"

- Fatty acids come from adipose tissue and are transported in blood, bound to albumen.
- Oxidation of fatty acids is one step in the "Metabolic Process" of the conversion of energy from fat to ATP.
  - This process spans several organs (Fig 11–7).
- Oxidation of fatty acids occurs in almost all tissues with mitochondria.
  - A notable exception is brain.
- Fatty acids are activated in the cytoplasm and then must enter the mitochondria for oxidation.
  - In muscle, oxidation of fatty acids is controlled by the rate of supply of FFA and by the need for ATP.
  - In liver, oxidation of fatty acids has 3 major controls:
    - The supply of FFA is an important control.
    - Low levels of glucose (mediated by low insulin which leads to a fall in the key inhibitor, malonyl CoA) stimulate the oxidation of fatty acids (a key control).
    - Oxidation of fatty acids can proceed faster than the need for acetyl–CoA for the synthesis of ATP, because excess acetyl–CoA can be converted to ketoacids.
- The rate of oxidation of fatty acids is inversely related to the rate of synthesis of fatty acids.

> • General Control:
>   - Oxidation of fatty acids provides the signals to inhibit the use of glucose and the activity of PDH.
>   - Oxidation occurs "Between meals and Without meals".
>   - Synthesis occurs "During meals".

FIGURE 11–8
CONTROL OF ENTRY OF FATTY ACYL GROUPS
INTO MITOCHONDRIA

The key step for regulation is whether malonyl–CoA is bound to its regulatory protein on the outside of mitochondria.

- The 4 components are:
  - The malonyl–CoA regulatory protein of CPT–1 on the outer mitochondrial membrane in liver.
  - Carnitine palmitoyl transferase–1 (CPT–1) on the inner aspect of the outer mitochondrial membrane.
  - Carnitine acyl–carnitine transferase which exchanges mitochondrial carnitine for cytoplasmic fatty acyl–carnitine.
  - CPT–2 inside the mitochondria regenerates fatty acyl–CoA inside the mitochondria.

KEY ROLE OF MALONYL–COA

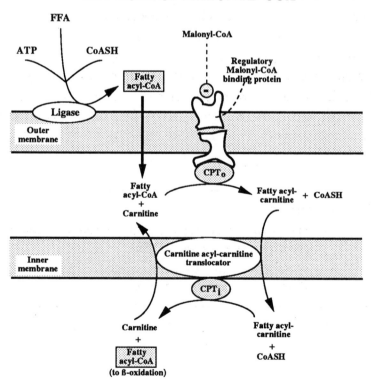

THE ENZYMES FOR THE OXIDATION OF FATTY ACIDS

- **Uptake of FFA from the circulation** (Fig 11–7)
  - Fatty acid–binding protein transports FFA from blood into the cell.
- **Activation of FFA** (formation of its CoA ester, Fig 11–8)
  - Occurs in the cytoplasm (the outer mitochondrial membrane).
  - ATP drives this reaction (acyl–CoA synthase).
  - The hydrolysis of 2 high energy bonds makes it irreversible.

$$FFA + CoASH + ATP \rightarrow FA\text{--}CoA + AMP + 2\,P_i$$

- **Fatty acyl–CoA crosses the inner mitochondrial membrane**

> - Carnitine is essential to transport fatty acyl units into mitochondria

- The 4 components that are involved are shown in Fig 11–8.

• The Reactions in the Oxidation of Fatty Acyl–CoA

> - Acetyl–CoA, NADH and $FADH_2$ are generated in each round of ß–oxidation

- This cycle splits off 2 carbon groups at a time until the fatty acid is fully broken down to acetyl CoA units.
- The reactions are shown in Fig 11–10:
  - Oxidation to enoyl–CoA yielding $FADH_2$
  - Hydration to hydroxy acyl–CoA
  - Oxidation to ketoacyl–CoA yielding $NADH + H^+$
  - Splitting off acetyl–CoA yielding an acyl–CoA 2 carbons shorter

• Stoichiometry

$$Palmitate + 7\,NAD^+ + 7\,FAD + 8\,CoASH \rightarrow 8\,Acetyl\text{--}CoA + 7\,NADH +$$
$$7\,H^+ + 7\,FADH_2$$

- Since each $NADH + H^+$ yields 3 ATPs and each $FADH_2$ yields 2 ATPs, ß–oxidation of palmitate yields 35 ATPs and complete oxidation to CO_2 yields 129 ATP (about 40% efficiency).

DISCUSSION OF CASE 11–2: BOB SUFFERS FROM FATIGUE

• **Synthesis of ATP in Muscle**

- Muscle derives its ATP for a few seconds from creatine–phosphate
- Then anaerobic glycolysis for the next 20–30 sec
- For the next while, it burns glucose to CO_2 in the TCA cycle
- None of these seem to be the problem
- Fatty acids are an important fuel later in exercise
- Thus Bob may not be able to burn fatty acids

• **Hypoglycemia Was Not Present**

- A lack of fatty acids in the blood would lead to excessive oxidation of glucose and symptoms of hypoglycemia
- This was not a problem on fasting, therefore he probably has enough fat for his liver, but muscle cannot use FFA

• **Levels of FFA Were High in the Blood**

- A biopsy of muscle revealed that there was a low level of carnitine–palmitoyl transferase in muscle.
- It was normal in the liver.

• Control Over Fatty Acid Oxidation

— A major control of fatty acid oxidation in all tissues is through the supply of FFA.

— The supply of FFA is mainly controlled by the activity of hormone sensitive lipase.

— In consumer organs (muscle, kidney), oxidation of FFA is limited by their need for ATP.

— The mechanism is probably through tying up of CoASH as acetyl–CoA in mitochondria (which inhibits PDH) and in fatty acyl–CoA in the cytoplasm.

— In maintainer organs (liver), an excess of acetyl–CoA can escape as ketoacids.

     — Since liver can both make and oxidize fatty acids, a further control is needed.

         — Malonyl–CoA the precursor of fatty acid synthesis, inhibits entry of fatty acyl–CoA through the mitochondrial membrane via the carnitine–linked carrier.

         — Hence, high glucose, through high insulin, stimulates the synthesis of fatty acids and inhibits the oxidation of fatty acids (and vice versa).

CASE 11–2:
BOB SUFFERS FROM FATIGUE

Bob, age 7, complains of extreme fatigue and pain in his muscles only when he does strenuous work and for a protracted period of time. These symptoms are easily reproduced by performing work of long duration only. Otherwise, he feels quite well. The above symptoms are not reproduced by a therapeutic fast or a quick sprint. How would you proceed to make a diagnosis?

Hint

His symptoms are primarily from muscle, so look here first. Determine what fuel he cannot burn and deduce whether this fuel is present in the circulation.

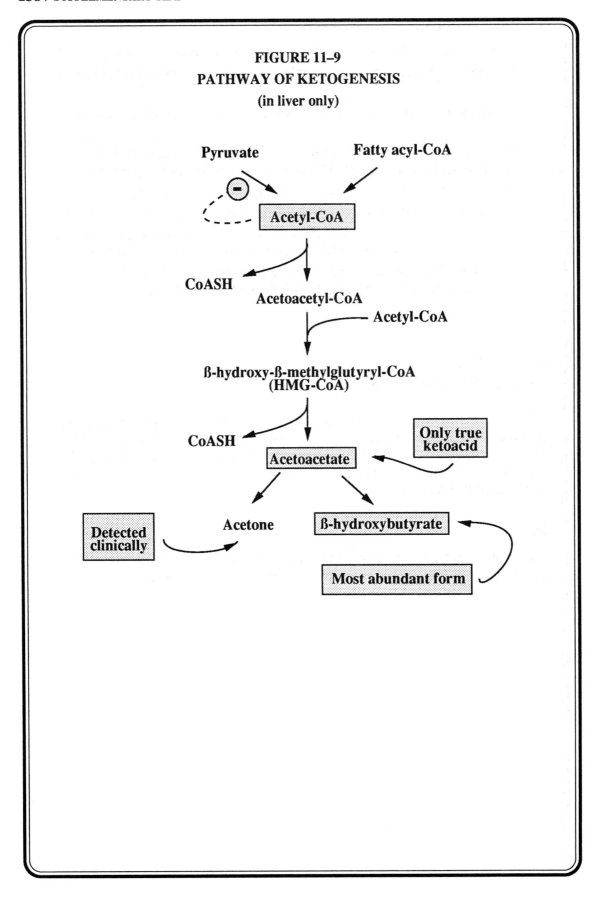

FIGURE 11–9
PATHWAY OF KETOGENESIS
(in liver only)

SYNTHESIS OF KETOACIDS

Synthesis of Ketoacids in Perspective
(Fig 11 – 9)

> • Ketoacids are formed in liver when the rate of formation of acetyl–CoA is excessively high (from ß–oxidation) and the liver does not need to synthesize ATP at that rapid a rate.

• Ketoacids are made only in the liver.

• Synthesis of ketoacids permits liver to form a water–soluble, fat–derived fuel so almost all organs can burn fuels derived from fat when the level of glucose is low.

• There is a net production of ATP during the synthesis of ketoacids from fatty acids.

$$\text{Palmitate} \rightarrow 4\text{ ß–Hydroxybutyrate} + 3\text{ NADH} + 7\text{ FADH}_2$$
$$\text{(9 ATP)} \qquad \text{(14 ATP)}$$

• Ketogenesis yields acids. Thus, an increased concentration of ketoacids in the blood adds a H^+ load which must be buffered. This is only a problem when metabolism of fat is totally out of control (lack of insulin during diabetic ketoacidosis).

Ketogenesis at the Enzyme Level

> • The main route of synthesis of ketoacids is through 3–hydroxy–3–methyl–glutaryl–CoA (HMG–CoA) in the liver (only).

• The 4 important enzyme reactions are:

 – Condense 2 acetyl–CoAs to acetoacetyl–CoA. This is catalyzed by the last enzyme of B–oxidation, ß–ketothiolase. This frees one CoASH.

 – HMG–CoA synthase uses a third acetyl–CoA. This frees a second CoASH.

 – HMG–CoA lyase splits HMG–CoA to yield acetoacetate, a CoASH–free metabolite that can cross membrane (rapidly if they have a carboxylate transporter) and acetyl–CoA.

 – ß–hydroxybutyrate dehydrogenase. This adds more potential ATP ($NADH + H^+$) to the exported ketoacids.

• Synthesis of ketoacids occurs in the mitochondria.

• **Stoichiometry:** 2 Acetyl–CoA $\rightarrow$ Acetoacetate + 2 CoASH.

FIGURE 11–10

PATHWAY OF OXIDATION OF KETOACIDS

(in brain, kidney and heart)

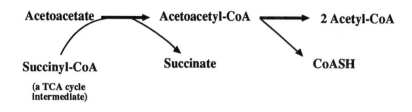

DISCUSSION OF QUESTION

For life–threatening ketoacidosis to be present, either the rate of synthesis of ketoacids must be excessively high or the rate of removal of ketoacids must be decreased (Chapter 6).

Synthesis of Ketoacids

* This is controlled in large fact by the supply of fatty acids and thus by HSL.
    – Main control, HSL is inhibited by insulin
* The second important site for control of ketogenesis is in the liver.
    – It is inhibited by insulin and stimulated by glucagon
* Since oxidation of ketoacids spares glucose, the concentration of glucose in the circulation will increase, causing release of some insulin and a slower rate of synthesis of ketoacids.
* In diabetes mellitus in very poor control, there is little if any insulin.
* An upper limit on hepatic ketogenesis is dictated by the the turnover of ATP in the liver (1600 mmol/day), since ketogenesis produces considerable ATP in liver.

Oxidation of Ketoacids

* About half of the ketoacids formed are consumed by the brain.
    – The rate is controlled primarily by the rate of turnover of ATP in the brain. In coma, or with anaesthesia, the rate of energy use by brain decreases and ketoacids accumulate
* As the work of the kidney declines, less ATP and thus less ketoacids are needed.
    – Work of the kidney declines when less sodium is filtered (and reabsorbed).
    – This occurs in diabetes mellitus in poor control (glycosuria) (Chapter 4)
* Controls (that we do not fully understand) permit skeletal muscle to oxidize FFA rather than ketoacids when the levels of both are high in the blood.

CONTROL OVER KETOGENESIS

> • Lack of insulin, via high malonyl–CoA, is the most important
> type of regulation of ketogenesis in the liver.

• The prime control is the supply of acetyl–CoA in liver mitochondria. This has a very powerful effect on the concentration of HMG–CoA by simple mass action – substrate supply effects.

• The rate of formation of ketoacids is limited by:

  – The concentration of fatty acids in the blood.

  – The level of malonyl–CoA in the liver which regulates the entry of fatty acid residues into the mitochondria.

  – The need of the liver for ATP.

Oxidation of ketoacids

> • Acetoacetate is a major fuel in brain, kidneys and heart when its
> level is high in the circulation.
>
> • It is converted to acetyl–CoA in mitochondria, in a reaction
> closely linked to the TCA cycle.

• **Enzyme Steps**
(Fig 11 – 10)

• Ketoacids enter mitochondria (via a transporter) and use CoA bound in a "high energy" form (succinyl–CoA).

• Acetoacetyl–CoA is the second last intermediate of ß–oxidation of fatty acid.

  – With free CoASH, 2 acetyl–CoA molecules are formed.

• If ß–hydroxybutyrate is the substrate, an extra NADH + H[+] is formed (+ 3 ATPs).

• **Control:** Use ketoacids if their concentration is high in the circulation.

  – This use is prevented in organs that oxidize FFA if the supply of FFA is also very high (skeletal muscle).

QUESTION

(Discussion on facing page)

Why are ketoacids not formed at high enough rates **"without meals"** to avoid life–threatening ketoacidosis?

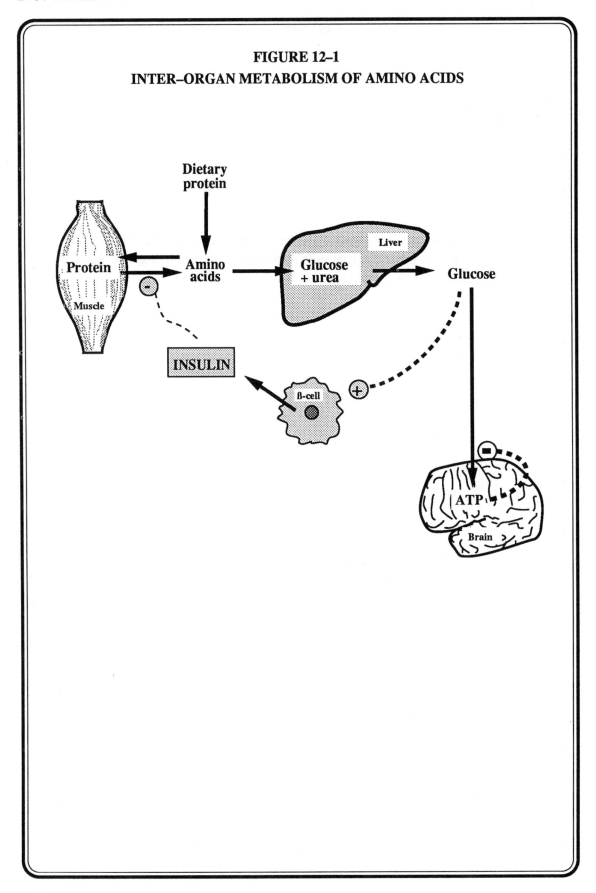

FIGURE 12–1
INTER–ORGAN METABOLISM OF AMINO ACIDS

CHAPTER 12

PROTEIN AND AMINO ACID METABOLISM

OVERVIEW

> - All proteins have specific functions, e.g. as enzymes.
> - Use of protein in the body for energy fuels is at the expense of function of tissues.
> - Metabolism of amino acids and proteins is of significance to energy metabolism because there is so much protein in the body.

- Protein and amino acid energy metabolism includes
  - Synthesis of proteins from amino acids
  - Breakdown of proteins to amino acids
  - Amino acid oxidation
- Each of these is very complex. Our intent here is to provide only an overview of the parts necessary to understand energy metabolism.

METABOLISM OF PROTEINS IN PERSPECTIVE (Fig. 12–1)

1. Synthesis of Proteins

- Proteins usually contain 20 amino acids, in chains.
  - Each protein has its own unique sequence of amino acids
  - The sizes of different proteins range from very small (a few amino acids in some peptide hormones) to very large (thousands of amino acids)
- There is constant synthesis and breakdown of proteins, through normal turnover of body components.
  - Hence amino acids are constantly entering and leaving energy metabolism
  - Because 9 amino acids are essential (not made in the body, and must come from the diet), synthesis of proteins without dietary protein can only be at the expense of other proteins in the body
  - Hence there is net loss of protein in fasting, which must be made back up in the fed state
- Each protein is synthesized on a template derived from its own gene through essentially the same process, but controls are unique for each protein, since each has its own unique function.
- Muscle contains the largest mass of protein; hence synthesis of proteins in muscle is the major factor in energy metabolism.

TABLE 12–1
FAMILIES OF AMINO ACIDS AND
THEIR KEY FEATURES

Families of Amino Acids	Feature
GLYCINE	• Used to detoxify (conjugations)
ALANINE	• N carrier to liver

3 BRANCHED–CHAIN
  VALINE
  LEUCINE
  ISOLEUCINE
	• All are fuels for muscle

2 HYDROXYLATED
  SERINE
  THREONINE
  TYROSINE – see later
	• All are phosphorylated for regulation

2 SULPHUR CONTAINING
  METHIONINE
  CYSTEINE
	• Linking of proteins
	• Production of acids

2 ACIDIC
  ASPARTIC ACID
  GLUTAMIC ACID
	• Intestinal fuel
	• Neurotransmitter
	• Anionic charge

2 WITH AMIDES
  ASPARAGINE
  GLUTAMINE
	• Kidney, Excretion of H^+

3 WITH AROMATIC RINGS
  PHENYLALANINE
  TYROSINE
 	
  TRYPTOPHAN
	• Synthesis of adrenaline
	• Phosphorylated in regulation
	• Neurotransmitter (serotonin)

3 BASIC AMINO ACIDS
  LYSINE
  ARGININE
  HISTIDINE
	• Cationic charge
	
	• Buffer

1 ATYPICAL amino acid PROLINE	• A lot in collagen

2. Breakdown of Proteins

- This is a simple hydrolysis of the protein to yield individual amino acids.

Net Balance

- The balance between the synthesis (**anabolism**) and breakdown or proteins (**catabolism**), in bulk terms, is controlled by hormones.
  - **Anabolism** is stimulated by insulin, some steroids (male), and growth hormone as long as there are amino acids available.
  - **Catabolism** is stimulated by glucocorticoids, thyroid hormone, glucagon, adrenaline, and many drugs.

METABOLISM OF AMINO ACIDS

Families of Amino Acids

- Amino acids can be classified into families based on their functions (Table 12–1)
  - Among the major families, we highlight
    - Those which can yield glucose (glucogenecic)
    - Those which cannot yield glucose (ketogenic)
    - Those with a hydroxyl group which can be phosphorylated and hence are important for regulation
    - Those with a hydrophobic side chain; these form the area of protein which spans a membrane
    - Those which confer charge to proteins (cationic or anionic)
    - That which is important for buffering (histidine)

- The many pathways for making, interconverting and breaking down amino acids can be found in any standard text.

Breakdown

- All amino acids break down to either
  - Precursors of glucose,
    - Pyruvate, oxalacetate, 2–oxoglutarate
  - Precursors of fat,
    - Acetyl–CoA
- All amino acids also release nitrogen (ultimately NH_4^+ or urea).
  - Hence breakdown of amino acids has a **CARBON** story and a **NITROGEN** story. These are linked in the formation of urea in the liver, and in the excretion of acid in the kidney (Chapter 2)

FIGURE 12–2
A QUANTITATIVE LOOK AT THE METABOLISM
OF AMINO ACIDS

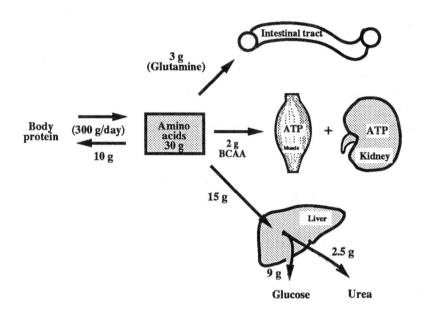

FIGURE 12–3
THE ROLE OF THE LIVER IN ENERGY METABOLISM

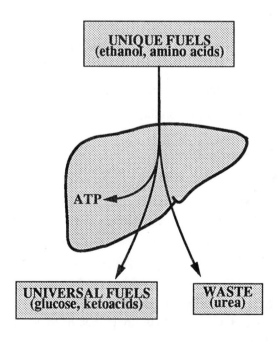

Location in Organs
(Fig 12–2)

- Oxidation of most of the amino acids occurs in the **liver**.
  - The liver also makes urea
  - The breakdown of sulphur–containing and dibasic amino acids (lysine, arginine) occurs in the liver to yield a net acid load

- Oxidation of branched–chain amino acids (isoleucine, leucine, valine) occurs mainly in **muscle**, producing alanine and glutamine.

- The **kidney** can break down glutamine.
  - This is essential for the excretion of net acid in urine (see Chapter 2)

- The **intestinal tract** consumes glutamine, glutamate and aspartate, to produce alanine.
  - It also hydrolyses approximately 25% of the urea made in liver

NITROGEN BALANCE

- Humans are in nitrogen balance when the amount of protein being synthesized equals the amount being degraded.
- Positive nitrogen balance means the body is depositing net protein; this is seen in growing children, or in recovery from a catabolic state.
- Nitrogen balance and positive nitrogen balance are only seen with the intake of protein.
- Negative nitrogen balance is a net loss of protein. It is seen when protein in the diet is not sufficieny, eg– illness, etc.
  - Even in negative nitrogen balance, there is some synthesis of protein
- In nitrogen balance turnover of proteins is dynamic.
  - A healthy adult synthesizes approximately 300 g of protein/day, while ingesting approximately 100 g of protein/day

Quantitative Analysis
- The average intake of proteins in a normal adult is 100 g per day, equivalent to 400 kcal.
- The liver consumes just over 300 kcal/day.
  - Therefore, even though the liver initiates the combustion of amino acids, it must export the majority of their kcal (as glucose) (Fig 12–3)

Transaminases

Use vitamin B_6 as a cofactor (pyridoxal phosphate).

Glycine can be converted to serine (in the kidney)

$$2\,\text{Glycine} \;\rightarrow\; \text{Serine} + NH_4^+ + CO_2$$

Serine and threonine can be deaminated directly.

$$\text{Serine} \;\rightarrow\; \text{Pyruvate} + NH_4^+$$
$$\text{Threonine} \;\rightarrow\; \text{2–Oxobutyrate} + NH_4^+$$

Disease Examples

The branched chain amino acids are metabolized to their corresponding ketoacids by transamination. They are next acted upon by a branched chain ketoacid decarboxylase. This enzyme may be missing or low in activity due to genetic reasons. The resulting disease is Maple Syrup Urine Disease.

Phenylketonuria

Disorders of **Phenylalanine** and **Tyrosine** metabolism. Others include albinism, tyrosinemia and alkaptonuria).

TABLE 12–2
TYPICAL AMINO ACID RATIOS

The number depicts how many molecules of each amino acid are present per 1000 molecules of all amino acids in a typical diet.

The capital letters show the 3 letter abbreviations for each amino acid.

* Shows "essential" amino acids, which cannot be made by humans.

Shows amino acids which cannot be made into glucose by humans.

ALAnine 82	HIStidine* 32	PROline 54
ARGinine 47	IsoLEucine*,# 51	SERine 51
ASPartate + ASparagiNe 89	LEUcine*,# 79	THReonine* 47
CYSteine 13	LYSine* 76	TRyPtophan* 24
GLUtamate + GLutamiNe 131	METhione* 21	TYRosine 24
GLYcine 105	PHEnylalanine* 32	VALine*,# 60

HYdroxyProline is made from proline during the synthesis of collagen.

OXIDATION OF AMINO ACIDS – ENZYME LEVEL

This is a 2–step process

1. Transfer nitrogen from amino acid to form glutamate (transamination)
2. Oxidative deamination of glutamate releases NH_4^+.

- The two main transaminases in liver are

   1. Alanine amino transferase

   Alanine + 2–Oxoglutarate $\leftrightarrow$ Glutamate + Pyruvate

   2. Aspartate amino transferase

   Aspartate + 2–Oxoglutarate $\leftrightarrow$ Glutamate + Oxaloacetate

   – The removal of nitrogen from half of the amino acids occurs by oxidative deamination of glutamate via glutamate dehydrogenase for form NH_4^+

   Glutamate + NAD^+ $\rightarrow$ 2–Oxoglutarate + NADH + H^+ + NH_4^+

   – The removal of the other half of the nitrogens occurs after they are converted to aspartate (reversing aspartate amino transferase above)

- Oxidation of amino acids has a **CARBON** story and a **NITROGEN** story.

1. Carbon Story of Oxidation of Amino Acids
(Table 12–2)

- A range of pathways breaks down the alpha–ketoacids to yield compounds which are used elsewhere in metabolism
   - Pyruvate or citric acid cycle intermediates which can be converted to glucose
   - Acetoacetyl–CoA or acetyl–CoA which cannot be converted to glucose
   - **Glucogenic amino acids are:**

      Alanine, threonine, glycine, serine, cysteine (via pyruvate), Arginine, histidine, glutamine, proline, glutamate (via 2–Oxoglutarate), Isoleucine, methionine, valine (via succinyl–CoA), Phenylalanine, tyrosine (via fumarate), Aspartate, asparagine (via oxalacetate).
   - **Ketogenic amino acids are:**

      Phenylalanine, tyrosine, leucine, lysine, tryptophan (via acetyl–CoA).

      Phenylalanine and tyrosine yield both fumarate and acetyl–CoA.

FIGURE 12–4
UREA CYCLE

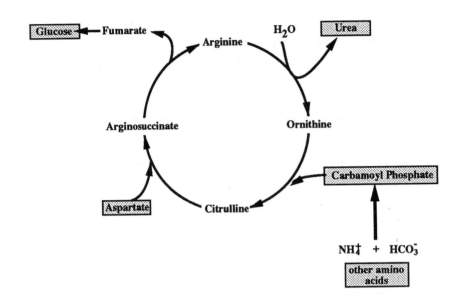

Urea synthesis is partly inside and partly outside mitochondria.

Mitochondrial reactions

- Glutamate → NH_4^+
- Carbamoyl–phosphate synthetase
- Ornithine transcarbamylase
- Aspartate synthesis (partly outside too)

Cytoplasmic reactions

- Argininosuccinate synthetase
- Argininosuccinase
- Arginase
- Fumarate to glucose

Transport steps across mitochondrial membrane

- Citrulline exit
- Ornithine entry
- Some pyruvate entry and aspartate exit

2. Nitrogen Story of Oxidation of Amino Acids
(Fig 12–3)

> - Urea is synthesized in the liver; half the nitrogen comes from NH_4^+ and half from aspartate.
> - The pathway is regulated by the load of nitrogen (NH_4^+).

- Stoichiometry

$$2\,NH_4^+ + 2\,HCO_3^- + 4.7\,ATP \;\rightarrow\; Urea + CO_2.$$

- The urea cycle was discovered by Krebs and Henseleit in 1932.
- The precursors are NH_4^+ + aspartate and the products are glucose + urea.
- **ATP requirement**
  - 2 ATPs are used for the synthesis of carbamoyl–phosphate
  - 2 ATPs are used for the synthesis of argininosuccinate
  - One third of an ATP bond is used for the transport of aspartate and another 1/3, possibly, to transport ornithine across the mitochondrial membrane
- A derivative of glutamate, N–acetyl–glutamate is required for the carbamoyl–phosphate synthase reaction.

Inherited Defects

- A defect in any step in the urea cycle can yield toxicity owing to the accumulation of NH_4^+.
- Reactions with surplus carbamoyl–phosphate are

Carbamoyl phosphate + aspartate $\rightarrow$ Orotic acid

  - Accumulation of orotic acid (or its excretion in the urine) may help define the site of a defect in the urea cycle (defect is after the synthesis of orotic acid rather than before it).

SELECTED READING

CHAPTER 1

Diamond JM. How to gamble on physiological requirements. NIPS 1:208-210, 1986.

Owen OE, Holup JL, D'Alessio DA, Craig ES, Polansky M, Smalley KJ, Kavle ED, Bushman MC, Owen LR, Mozzoli MA, Kendrick ZV, Boden GH. A reappraisal of the caloric requirements of men. Am J Clin Nutr 46:875-885, 1987.

Rivlin RS, Shils ME, Sherlock P. Nutrition and cancer. Am J Med 75:843-854, 1983.

Shulman RG. Emerging techniques: High resolution NMR in vivo. TIBS 13:37-39, 1988.

VanderLars WJ, Elzinga G, Woledge RC. Energetics at the single cell level. NIPS 4:91-93, 1989.

CHAPTER 2

Brosnan JT, Lowry M, Vinay P, et al. Renal ammonium production-une vue Canadienne. Can J Physiol Pharm 65:489-498, 1987.

Halperin ML, Jungas RL. Metabolic production and renal disposal of hydrogen ions. Kidney Internat 24:709-713, 1983.

Halperin ML, Jungas RL, Cheema-Dhadli S, Brosnan JT. Disposal of the daily acid load; an integrated function of the liver, lungs and kidneys. TIBS 12:197-199, 1987.

CHAPTER 3

Newsholme E, Leech T. The Runner. Fitness Books, 1983

CHAPTER 4

Brownlee M, Cerami A, Vlassara H. Advanced glycosylation end products in tissue and the basis of diabetic complications. New Engl J Med 318:1315-1321, 1988.

Cerami A, Vlassara H, Brownlee M. Glucose and aging. Sci Amer 256:90-96, 1987.

Greene DA, Lattimer SA, Simms AAF. Sorbitol, phosphoinositides, and sodium-potassium-ATPase in the pathogenesis of diabetic complications. N Engl J Med 316:599-606, 1987.

CHAPTER 5

Hale PJ, Nattrass M. Metabolic profiles in patients with insulinoma. Clin Endocr 30:29-38, 1989.

Jaspan JB. Hypoglycemia: fact or fiction? Hospital Practice 24:11-14, 1989.

Jeevanandam M, Horowitz GD, Lowry SF, Brennan MF. Cancer cachexia and the rate of whole body lipolysis in man. Metabolism 35:304-310, 1986.

Palardy J, Havrankova J, Lepage R, Matte R, Belanger R, D'Amour P, Ste-Marie L. Blood glucose measurements during symptomatic episodes in patients with suspected postprandial hypoglycemia. N Engl J Med 321:1421-1425.

Service FJ, van Heerden JA, Sheedy PF. Insulinoma. In: Hypoglycemic Disorders (ed FJ Service), pp. 111-128, 1983. Hall Medical Boston, Mass.

CHAPTER 6

Flatt JP. On the maximal possible rate of ketogenesis. Diabetes 21:50-53, 1972.

Halperin ML, Cheema-Dhadli S. Renal and hepatic aspects of ketoacidosis.: a quantitative analysis based on energy turnover. Diabetes/Metabolism Rev 5:321-336, 1989.

Halperin ML, Fields ALA. Lactic acidosis-emphasis on the carbon precursors and buffering of the acid load, Amer J Med Sci 289:154-159, 1985.

Madias NE. Lactic acidosis. Kidney Internat 29:752-774, 1986.

Oh M, Carroll HJ. The anion gap. New Engl J Med 297:814-817, 1977.

Owen OE, Caprio S, Reichard GA Jr et al. Ketosis of starvation: a revisit and new perspectives. Endiocrinol Metab. 12:359-379, 1983.

Robinson AM, Williamson DH. Physiological aspects of the regulation of ketogenesis. Physiol Rev 60:143-187, 1980.

CHAPTER 7

Berridge MJ. The molecular basis of communication with the cells. Sci Amer 253:142-152, 1985

Crabtree B, Newsholme EA. A systematic approach to describing and analysing metabolic control systems. TIBS 12:4-12, 1987.

Kacser H, Portius JW. Control of metabolism: What do we measure? TIBS 12:5-14, 1987.

Pelech SL, Vance DE. Signal transduction via phosphatidylcholine cycles. TIBS 14:28-30, 1989

Rolleston FS. A theoretical background to the use of measured concentrations of intermediates in study of the role of intermediary metabolism. Current Topics in Cell Reg 5:47-75, 1972.

Tonks NK, Charbonneau H. Protein tyrosine dephosphorylation and signal transduction. TIBS 14:497-500, 1989.

CHAPTER 8

Bosca L, Corredor, C. Is phosphofructokinase the rate limiting step in glycolysis? TIBS 9:372-373, 1984

Hers HG, Hue L. Gluconeogenesis and related aspects of glycolysis. Ann Rev Biochem 52:617-653, 1983

Hers HG, VanSchaftigan E. Fructose 2,6-bisphosphate two years after its discovery. Biochem J 206:1-12, 1982

Hue L. The role of futile cycles in the regulation of carbohydrate metabolism in the liver. Adv Enzymol 52:247-330, 1981.

Katz J, Kuwajima M, Foster DW, McGarry JD. The glucose paradox: new perspectives on hepatic carbohydrate metabolism. TIBS 11:136-140, 1986.

Krauss-Friedman N. Hormonal control of gluconeogenesis. Vols I and II, CRC Press, 1986.

Pilkus SJ, Mahgrabi ML, Claus TH. Hormonal regulation of hepatic gluconeogenesis and glycolysis. Annu Rev Biochem 57:755-783, 1988.

Sprang SR, Acharya KR, Goldsmith EJ, Stuart DI, Varvill K, Fletterick RJ, Madsen NB, Johnson LN. Structural changes in glycogen phosphorylase induced by phosphorylation. Nature 336:215-221, 1988.

Walmsley AR. The dynamics of the glucose transporter. TIBS 13:226-231, 1988.

Widdas WF. Old and new concepts of the membrane transport for glucose in cells. Biochim Biophys Acta 947:385-404, 1988.

CHAPTER 9

Denton RM, Halestrap AP. Regulation of pyruvate metabolism in mammalian tissues. Essays Biochem. 15:37-77, 1979.

Fields ALA, Cheema-Dhadli S, Wolman SL, Halperin ML. Theoretical aspects of weight loss in patients with cancer. Cancer 50:2183-2188, 1982.

CHAPTER 10

Hatefi Y. The mitochondrial electron transport system and oxidative phosphorylation system. Ann Rev Biochem 54:1015-1069, 1985

Krebs HA. The history of the tricarboxylate cycle. Perspect Biol Med 14:154-170, 1970

Mitchell P. Coupling of phosphorylation to electron and hydrogen ion transfer by a chemiosmotic type of mechanism. Nature 191:144-148, 1961

Nicholls DG. Bioenergetics. Academic Press, 1982.

Nicholls DG, Rial E. Brown fat mitochondria. TIBS 9:489-491, 1984

Racker E. From Pasteur to Mitchell, a hundred years of bioenergetics. Fed Proc 39:210-215, 1980

CHAPER 11

Bieber LL. Carnitine. Annu Rev Biochem 88:261-283, 1988.

Ferguson SJ. Towards a mechanism for the ATP synthase of oxidative phosphorylation. TIBS 11:100101, 1986.

Hardie DG, Carling D, Sim ATR. The AMP-activated protein kinase: a multisubstrate regulator of lipid metabolism. TIBS 14:20-23, 1989.

McGarry JD, Foster DW. Regulation of hepatic fatty acid oxidation and ketone body production. Annu Rev Biochem 49:395-420, 1980.

Pande SV, Murthy MSR. Carnitine: vitamin for an insect, vital for man. Biochem Cell Biol 67:671-673, 1989.

CHAPTER 12

Bender DA. Amino acid metabolism. Wiley, 1985.

Cohen PP. The ornithine-urea cycle: biosynthesis and regulation of carbamyl phosphate synthetase I and ornithin transcarbamylase. Curr Top Cell Regul 18:1-19, 1981.

INDEX